WITH

SALE

THE OLD CENTURY

by the same author

*

MEMOIRS OF A FOX-HUNTING MAN

SHERSTON'S PROGRESS

THE COMPLETE MEMOIRS OF GEORGE SHERSTON

THE OLD CENTURY

SIEGFRIED'S JOURNEY

COLLECTED POEMS 1908–1956

THE OLD CENTURY

and seven more years

by

SIEGFRIED SASSOON

with an introduction by

MICHAEL THORPE

FABER AND FABER LIMITED
24 Russell Square
London

First published in mcmxxxviii
by Faber and Faber Limited
24 Russell Square London WC1
First published in this edition mcmlxviii
Printed in Great Britain by
Latimer Trend & Co Ltd Whitstable
All rights reserved

To
my friend
MAX BEERBOHM

CONTENTS

BOOK I

THE OLD CENTURY

INTRODUCTION

When *The Old Century* appeared in 1938 it was
greeted with rapturous reviews acclaiming its
'warm simplicity', enchantment—a recurrent word
—its miraculous perfection of the art that conceals
art: 'The bloom on the book is as if a hand had
never been on it', wrote H. M. Tomlinson, author
of *The Sea and the Jungle* and himself no mean
stylist. Yet rapturous reviews are all too often
poured out upon mediocre books. *The Old Century*
is no such book, but the tenor of its acclaim had
perhaps a particular significance. The actual date
of publication was September 15th, 1938, so that
it appeared in a crucial month in a tense year of
apprehension—such as, nowadays, has become
commonplace. On September 29th the Chamber-
lain government achieved the humiliating 'ap-
peasement' of Nazi Germany and won a brief
breathing-space before the outbreak of war
almost a year later. The breathing was fitful, the

strain was to increase: what more understandable
than that such a book as Sassoon's should have
been greeted in a manner expressive of the current
mood of relief? For older readers, faced with an
imminent second cataclysm in their lifetime, *The
Old Century* revived purely happy memories of the
late Victorian and early Edwardian 'golden afternoon', of the peaceful, slow years before the burst-
ing of the dykes on August 4th, 1914. For
younger readers, perhaps, the tranquil world it
portrayed symbolised their birthright, which had
been cast away by the folly of the Great War and
utterly submerged beneath the social upheaval and
widespread disillusion that followed it. The
literature between the wars reflected this bitter
state of affairs and offered little that one could, in
Matthew Arnold's phrase, 'rest upon'—however
briefly.

Should it, it will be asked, have done so?
Surely the consolation *The Old Century* offered
was an anachronism; it was a retrospect in which
'distance', essentially, '[lent] enchantment to the
view'. That afternoon only *seems* 'golden', those
peaceful years (1886-1907) were years of unprece-
dented materialism and ostentation for the indifferent few, poverty and wretchedness for many;
there were the inglorious Boer War, the rising,
combative trades unions, the militant suffragettes:
a divided country drifted toward her self-created

downfall. This is, substantially, the historian's view today, which only confirms the more heavily shaded literary versions projected throughout the first forty years of this century in such depths-plumbing books as Jack London's East End documentary, *The People of the Abyss* (1903), Mrs. Cecil Chesterton's *In Darkest London* (1926) and George Orwell's *The Road to Wigan Pier*, which came out just one year before *The Old Century*. As C. E. Montague wrote in his cool-eyed *Disenchantment* (1922), those Elysian years before the Great War were only 'Elysian for anyone who was not poor' —and in Orwell's work especially we see how little improved was the social condition by the time Sassoon came to write *The Old Century*. How, then, is it possible to defend the kind of book it was—and is, today, when any work to which the label 'escapist' can be pinned is especially liable to be hacked to pieces by the moralizing critic's scalpel?

Literature is not a branch of history or sociology, neither is autobiography necessarily the literal record of a life, if such a thing were possible—witness Conrad's disarmingly entitled *A Personal Record*. Life and his own experience furnish the artist's raw material, which he may shape as he chooses, providing he does not present the result as the total reality—then he exposes himself to justifiable attack. Sassoon had, on the surface, good reason for taking the 'golden afternoon' view. He was brought up in easy circumstances, in a beautiful, sequestered part of the Weald of Kent, then quite unsullied by modern 'developments' or degradations. Even the agricultural depressions which, in the 1890s, severely afflicted many areas of rural England left Kent relatively untouched (this is convincingly maintained by his fellow man of Kent and long-standing friend, Edmund Blunden, in his essays on the county). There is no reason why the self-contained, inviolate world portrayed here should not have seemed so in fact to the growing boy and youth. There was personal tragedy and loss: his father separated from his mother when Siegfried was five ('I wanted to enjoy my parents simultaneously—not alternately') and died four years later. Against this background the aspiring child poet's morbid fascination with Death is probably presented here with restraint: but the mother's love and devotion evidently went far to compensate for the father's loss and it is this that is stressed.

Sassoon does, in fact, confess to the reader his deliberate emphasis upon the happier elements: 'I feel the unbending visages of the realists reproving me for failing to imitate their awful and astringent example. Let me, therefore, be on the safe side, and offer a semi-apologetic confession of my inability to describe my early life in a dismal and dissatisfied tone of voice. All human beings desire to be glad. I prefer to remember my own gladness and good luck'. His theme is gladness, the glad aspects of his early life, and it is these he *prefers* to perpetuate.

Readers will interpret this approach in various ways and it is a very complex thing. The author, fashioning the life recalled to an image he values, has produced an unashamed idealization, not so much of that historical abstraction, Victorian or Edwardian life, as of his own early experience. It has the quality of a dream and the 'old century', as such, never existed: 'The past ought always to be like this', is his wistful reflection upon an idyllic retrospect in *The Weald of Youth*. The creative process involved here may be termed emotively 'escapism' or, in the clinical language of Freud, the satisfaction of the 'pleasure principle', which has often been imaged in literature as a paradisal garden 'where life is easiest for man': images suggesting this are established on the opening pages and underlie the whole narrative. Sassoon had certainly endured his infernal vision, as his painful war writings testify, but he would not wish this seductive dream to be taken for paradisal in the spiritual sense: this, for him, was to be long delayed, and the reader who turns to his poetry can trace his arduous 'way of the soul' there. *The Old Century* is a tale of innocence, not of experience.

In 1938, this dreamlike evocation of the past

undoubtedly answered a psychological need, in him and in his readers. Seventy years before, a writer who charmed him away from the History Tripos at Cambridge, William Morris, had written *The Earthly Paradise* in a strikingly similar state of mind: 'I can't enter into politico-social subjects with any interest', Morris had said, 'for on the whole I see that things are in a muddle, and I have no power or vocation to set them right in ever so little a degree. My work is the embodiment of dreams.' Later, Morris did plunge into the 'politico-social' muddle, whereas Sassoon had been through it all—war, socialism, political journalism —and was seeking rest from it. Is rest in the wishful dream desirable? Perhaps not: but refreshment is —submit oneself consciously and provisionally to dreams and one may carry away from them much that is substantial and restorative. Today we may respond to *The Old Century* more purely in this way than was possible for many of its readers thirty years ago.

Sassoon has himself described his book as 'a happy dream, which relieved my troubled mind' and which 'I wrote [in the winters of 1936 and 1937] deliberately to afford people nostalgic escape in those years of imminent catastrophe'; accordingly, 'the limitations of my recollections were deliberate and consistent'. His nostalgia was open-eyed. Now, as then, the Hades shadow falls from without across the scrupulous margins of the book: but the extremely nostalgic response of those many early readers for whom the dream and the reality were inextricably interwoven will hardly be shared by a younger generation. It is for them to judge coolly whether, regardless of the author's original intention, *The Old Century* remains (as I think) an humane, sensitive and beautifully written book which bears throughout the seal of the transforming imaginative power.

★   ★   ★

The Old Century is one of the most *inward* autobiographical narratives of childhood and the slow, organic process of growth into greater awareness of the world outside oneself that we have in English. It stands out even in a period which has practically invented such narratives: one thinks of those by Sir Edmund Gosse, Sassoon's patron in his youth, whose *Father and Son* is the great forerunner, by Richard Church, Joyce Cary, Sir L. E. Jones, Laurie Lee, Edwin Muir, Sir Herbert Read, Sir Osbert Sitwell, W. B. Yeats and, in fictional form, L. P. Hartley. Like these at their best, it is keenly visualized and impressionistic, unblemished by intrusive rationalization or hindsight. So completely is Sassoon absorbed in recollection in the early chapters that the balanced narrator's tone may slip almost imperceptibly into the child's breathless reportage: 'When we got there we had a glorious time with our grown-up girl cousins and their school-boy brother Tom, who had a little sailing-boat of his own and had built himself a crow's nest at the top of a lime tree and knew all about bird's eggs'. He is remarkably successful in his 'efforts to feel childish when childhood was my theme'. He also faithfully conveys the mixed nature of childish feeling towards the claims of others, their sadness or loss, without crediting the child, as autobiographers are prone to do, with precocious sensitivity or insight. The period of adolescence and early youth is traced with equal faithfulness, again without forcing development or giving spurious shape to the unformed character.

It will, however, become obvious to the reader that the other people in the book have been drawn selectively, in accord with the writer's desire to remember 'my own gladness and good luck'. 'My intention has been to commemorate or memorialize those human contacts which supported me in my rather simple-minded belief that the world was full of extremely nice people if only one could get to know them properly'. 'Memorialize' is a word that may mislead—for the dream, albeit idealized, is always kept in essential touch with flesh and blood. Most memorable amongst many

18

sympathetic portraits are those of 'The Teacher', 'frugal and unenvious', and 'Wirgie', whose niceness is tempered with a bracing, astringent candour.

The whole narrative has a marked pictorial quality, which is felt cumulatively both in the visual force of countless small details and in longer, concentrated passages that, borrowing Wordsworth's phrase, we may call 'spots of time'. These passages, devoted mainly to natural description, have two principal effects: they establish the tranquil and mellow atmosphere, recapturing the very 'texture of time' (p. 20) and also symbolize crucial moments in the growth of the young sensibility. (The method and the poetic quality of the prose are akin to Virginia Woolf's handling of the time motif in her novels, *The Years* and *The Waves*). The vivid well- and sowing-scenes which form the Prelude to Book I set the pattern. These give the child's-eye view, close to nature, the source, wondering and finding wonder in the common mysteries that will become woven into the very texture of his awareness. They provide a poetic metaphor to herald life in its beginnings: 'And the purpose of this book is to tell whither the water journeyed from its source, and how the seed came up'. This opening, with its rooted imagery and harmonious sense of growth, is answered by the tenor of the closing chapter of Book II, within which are gathered, on the twenty-first birthday, all the scents, sounds, colours and marks of the life approaching a turning point. Between these twin poles lie many other such passages: especially memorable are the revisitations to the old home Weirleigh, in reverie, and in actuality—though it seems dream-like—to Edingthorpe, the family's Norfolk holiday village in 1897. The Edingthorpe chapter (Book I, Chapter VIII) best epitomises the nostalgic spirit and the power of recall pervading the whole book. It also provides a striking case of cooperation between actuality and the dream: the author has described the revisitation as 'exact in every detail. I never saw a soul, all the time I was there, as though it had been specially laid on for me to write about'—and no one who has passed through any such tiny Norfolk village on a midsummer afternoon, even today, will be disposed to doubt the likelihood of this.

As a stylist, Sassoon inherits the tradition established by the many nineteenth century writers who stressed perfection of form. Notable amongst these (for our purposes) is Walter Pater. In *The Weald of Youth*, after a short passage in imitation of Pater's style, Sassoon refers to 'my continued enjoyment of everything he wrote'. There is a marked affinity between his manner of recalling his childhood and Pater's in the brief memoir *The Child in the House*. Both accent the sensuous intensity of the child's awareness, his living very much within himself and his lasting attachment to his early surroundings as, in Pater's words, to 'a place "inclosed" and "sealed".' Pater recalls the *old house*, as Sassoon does the old century, fixed in another irretrievable existence; his Florian, in words equally applicable to Sassoon's mode of recollection, remembers the loved old place in 'a dream which did him the office of a finer sort of memory, bringing its object to mind with a great clearness, yet, as sometimes happens in dreams, raised a little above itself, and above ordinary retrospect'.

The style Sassoon partly inherits from Pater is currently out of fashion. Yet he has good company amongst a great many modern writers who have explored the possibilities of 'prose poetry': to name a few, Henry James, James Joyce, W. B. Yeats—who opened the *Oxford Book of Modern Verse* in 1936 with the Gioconda passage from Pater's *The Renaissance*—Edward Thomas, Virginia Woolf and Max Beerbohm, to whom *The Old Century* was dedicated in appreciation of his generous help in giving the work its final polish. Poetic prose undoubtedly has its vices: it is always liable to the charge of purple passagery or—that abused cant word—'insincerity', which is best understood as an excessive concern with how, at the expense of what, you say (a fault by no means peculiar to this,

or any, style). But this was Pater's vice: his pro-
tracted periods often generate a monotonous flow
which submerges meaning. Whether or not *The Old
Century* incurs the dangers of its style the reader
will wish to judge for himself, in responding to the
book to which I should now leave him. I shall
close by quoting some catholic words of Pater's,
both to defend this unfashionable book's right to
an unprejudiced reading for its own unique merits
—on grounds apparently recognized by its admirably catholic publishers—and to make some
amends to Pater himself:

'In truth the legitimate contention is, not of one
age or school of literary art against another, but
of all successive schools alike, against the stupidity
which is dead to the substance, and the vulgarity
which is dead to form'.

MICHAEL THORPE.

May 1967

Note: I am grateful to Leiden University Press for
permission to use material from my *Siegfried
Sassoon: A Critical Study* in this Introduction.
M.T.

PRELUDE

Far off in earliest-remembered childhood I can overhear myself repeating the words 'Watercress Well'. I am kneeling by an old stone well-head; my mother is standing beside me and we are looking into the water. My mother tells me that it is 'a very deep-rising spring'; but I do not want to be told anything about it, even by her. I want nothing at all except to be gazing at the water which bubbles so wonderfully up out of the earth, and to dip my fingers in it and scatter the glittering drops.

From its well-head the spring overflows into cressy shallows; thence it wanders away as a gurgling and purposeful runnel which may, some day, for all I can tell, arrive at being a real Kentish river. The well reflects the empty sky; I can see myself in it, rather obscurely, when I am not watching the bubbles climbing up in the middle of the crystal-clear water.

Many a half-hour's pilgrimage we made from our house to Watercress Well, which, after having been one of my 'favourite places to go to', now becomes a symbol of life itself in an opaque and yet transparent beginning. From that so intensely remembered source all my journeyings now seem to have started. If I were to go back and look for it I might find that it has vanished; but in my thoughts it is for ever the same. Around and above it whisper the woodland branches; time's wavering shadows are falling across the glade; but there will be no sunset for that pictured afternoon. Light as a leaf, a robin drops down and decides to have a drink. I look again; the robin is not there. The well-head is alone with its secret energy of life. My mother and I are voices out of sight, for we are half-way across a breezy meadow, leaving behind us Watercress Well and the rivulet that goes running through the wood, talking to itself in the wordless language of water and roots and stones.

*   *   *

Again, from those lost years of childhood, I hear my voice. This time it asks a question. 'What will the seeds be like when they come up?' I am standing beside my mother, who is making a water-colour sketch of a man sowing. It is a dry bright morning in early spring and we are sheltered from the cold east wind by the catkined hazels of a little copse where I have been picking primroses.

The ploughed land slopes upward. Marching across it, the sower in his sackcloth apron scoops and scatters the seed from a wooden trug on his left arm, providing my mother with a simple picture, for he has only the brown field and the blue sky behind him. A grand hale-looking man he is, like someone out of the Bible—Abraham, perhaps —and two of his sturdy sons are there to help him. One of them is a waggoner, and presently he will give me a ride up the lane.

'What will the seeds be like when they come up?' Recovered in my clear memory of that spring morning, the words now seem like part of a parable. And the purpose of this book is to tell whither the water journeyed from its source, and how the seed came up.

I

On the varnished pinewood door of our day-nursery there were some ruled lines with pencilled dates written above them. At intervals of a few inches these lines recorded the earliest stature of my two brothers and myself, and up to 1893 they were, so to speak, the only mark I had made in the world. I do not know exactly how high I was in 1893, but some time during that year I also began to scribble marks on paper which signified that I aspired to be an author. 'Once upon a time.' Those must have been the first words I wrote with this intent, since the ~~Blue Fairy~~ Book was my model and most of the stories I had read or listened to had started like that. Had I been less fanciful and writing my own story, I should have begun as follows. 'Once upon a time there was a boy who was born in September 1886 at a house in Kent where he has lived ever since. He had two brothers

26

who were born in 1884 and 1887, but we all behaved as if we were the same age. After 1891 we
did not see our father very often. Our mother was
unhappy because he had gone away to live in London and would not speak to her any more. Our
nurse, whose name was Mrs. Mitchell, did not tell
us why this had happened.'

Such were the bare details, which serve to show
that my early awareness of the world began with a
confused knowledge that I was living in a family
story which did not promise to have a happy ending. For even at six or seven years old I could feel
that the situation was uncomfortable. But my most
real regret was that we saw our father so seldom.

I will describe one of his visits. On some afternoon of the spring of 1892 we would all three of us,
in clean white smocks, be flattening our noses
against the nursery window with our eyes on the
front gate (near which a large magnolia tree was in
flower). When 'Pappy' was at last seen getting
out of the village fly there would be shrill acclama-
tions and wavings at the window. Soon he would
come quickly along the nursery passage and we
would crowd excitedly round him, unrestrained by
Mrs. Mitchell's admonitions. 'Pappy' was a dark-
haired youngish man with large sad brown eyes
and a moustache which tickled when he kissed you.
His clothes smelt of cigar smoke, and the amber

and gold mouthpiece in his waistcoat pocket was an object of interest—more so even than his signet ring and the other one with the brown diamond. He brought interesting parcels containing things we'd never eaten before, such as guava jelly or a pomegranate, and funny toys which didn't need too much taking care of; he romped with us on the floor and made screamingly funny jokes, and was altogether a perfect papa while his visit lasted, which wasn't long, for all too soon he looked at his gold repeater watch and began to talk about catching the train back to London. While he was having his tea by the nursery fire we stood rather solemnly round him, and if I was lucky he gave me the top of his egg. Meanwhile Mrs. Mitchell, with her hard gipsy face, was extremely ingratiating and spoke in a voice which wasn't the same as her everyday one. And when he left us there would be a confabulation in undertones half-way along the passage, while we wondered what they were saying and whether it was about 'Mamsy'. In the first months of their final estrangement we used to tell 'Mamsy' about his visits and how he had pretended to be a dromedary or a bear. I can remember the episode which brought home to me the unhappiness of her experience. She used to shut herself up in the drawing-room when my father came, but one autumn afternoon we were out in the garden and he was giving us a ride in the gardener's handcart. We were all three shouting and thoroughly enjoying ourselves when we came round the corner of some rhododendrons and met my mother, whose self-repression had perhaps relaxed and had released her in the forlorn hope of some sort of reconciliation. Anyhow, there she stood and we all went past her in sudden silence. I have never forgotten the look on her face. It was the first time I had seen life being brutal to someone I loved. But I was helpless, for my father's face had gone blank and obstinate, and the situation, like the handcart, was in his hands. All I could do was to feel miserable about it afterwards and wonder why they couldn't make it up somehow. For I wanted to enjoy my parents simultaneously—not alternately.

I suppose that as time went on my brothers and I must have got used to things being as they were. The summer of 1893 was memorably fine and I still connect it with open-air happiness. I seem to remember being taken out at night to see a comet —or it may have been the Aurora Borealis. And I know that we gave 'a grand feast' for my mother, in the garden on August 4th, which was my younger brother's sixth birthday, because the invitation still exists—an elaborate document which I wrote with my coloured chalk pencils and decorated profusely with drawings of hop-kilns and garden implements.

After that my father began to be obviously ill. His cough got worse and worse, and soon he went to stay at Eastbourne. Early in 1894 Mrs. Mitchell took us there for several weeks. 'Pappy' used to talk quite gaily about being well again soon and taking us abroad with him, but he was dreadfully thin; his face looked transparent and his light-coloured clothes hung loosely on him. Once a week he was weighed and though we always hoped to hear that he had put on a pound or two he never had, and Mrs. Mitchell's relish for the lugubrious made her unable to conceal the fact that he was 'in a galloping consumption'.

Much as I trusted in my prayers being heard I couldn't quite believe that God was able to cure 'Pappy' of consumption. Lying in bed I did a lot of extra praying, but there must have been moments when I half-consciously connected the sound of incoming waves with the idea of death; I may even have remembered my morning's work on the sands and how I'd watched the sea washing away my carefully patted little fortifications.

Eastbourne was full of compensations, however; we squabbled among ourselves much less than when we were at home, and Mrs. Mitchell's temper was notably improved by the change of scene.

Taking us up on to Beachy Head, or to the public gardens to hear the band, she seldom lapsed from amiability, and almost every day we had shrimps for tea.

Before we returned home 'Pappy' took us to the photographer's. After some vigorous combing and brushing of our hair by Mrs. Mitchell, 'Pappy' looked at the camera for the last time and a rather pathetic picture was taken.

My younger brother, who had dark corkscrew curls, was sitting on his knee, and we all 'came out' much too tidy and smirksome to be real. The only reality was in my father's face. About that the camera told the truth.

The summer of 1894 increased my experience of life by being a wet one, but it was monotonous experience, for how could anything interesting happen when we were always being kept indoors? Although we were quite good at keeping ourselves amused in the house there was a great deal of time on our hands of which I now, quite naturally, remember nothing, except that it was like going for rides on the dapple-grey rocking-horse, for which I was now getting too old. On fine days we spent nursery-oblivious hours at the edge of the garden, down by the wood. There we had built ourselves a ramshackle shanty which kept the rain out and was known as 'The Build', a name which had originated from a hundred real red bricks which my mother had bought for us to begin it with. My ambition was that 'The Build' should some day have a second storey, which I imagined as a long loft containing sacks of malt. Of malt I knew nothing, but I liked the idea of it. There, at any rate, we secluded ourselves, sowed tomatoes and nasturtiums, which never came up, and on special occasions invited my mother and Mrs. Mitchell to tea. Thence we sallied forth to cause what annoyance we could to the head gardener, Mr. Reeves, who was a short hasty-tempered man with a beard and a brown bowler hat. We were on good terms with the two under-gardeners, Mabb and Ely, who tolerated our potato-throwing pranks good-humouredly; but to be chased out of the potting-shed and down to the edge of the wood by Reeves was considered very good sport, and to crawl in through the vinery window after he had gone home, and borrow the squirt, always led to satisfactory results. All this made up for the blank hours in bad weather when I sat on the window-sill in the nursery passage, and the texture of time consisted of a smell of ivy and elder bushes, and the noise of sparrows quarrelling, and an intense longing to be grown-up and able to do what one liked.

Winter, of course, couldn't help being more monotonous. Up to Christmas of that year only two things happened which could be called exciting. First of all our apple-house was robbed and no one ever found out who did it. And about the same time there was the alarm about burglars. A real burglary had happened a few miles away, so the idea was in the air. Not long afterwards I awoke in the middle of the night to become aware that the burglars had been trying to get in; Mrs. Mitchell was sure she had heard them. Leaning over the banisters in our nightgowns we watched her as she moved about the front hall with a candlestick, talking to my mother in a gruff voice so as to make the burglars think that there was a man in the house. Finally my mother marched out of the pump-yard door with an air-gun under her arm attended by a shivering maid with a lantern. 'Come out,' she said in a loud and determined voice, and fired the air-gun into some bushes.

Nothing happened; but the burglars had to be believed in, though no evidence of their visit was discovered next day. It was after this adventure that the large deep-toned alarm bell was attached to an upper part of the house above the pump-yard, as a sort of assistant to the lightning conductor.

The pump-yard, by the way, was where the well was. The well was sixty feet deep, and supplied all our water. Every morning two of the gardeners worked the double-handled pump for an hour. We used to enjoy watching Mr. Reeves pumping because we knew that he didn't like doing it. When we pushed the window up and asked him whether he was getting hot he used to say that he hoped Mrs. Mitchell would give us a good leathering before we were much older. On the far side of the pump-yard a large fig tree grew up the wall; so I have never smelt a fig tree since without the words pump-yard coming into my head.

In those days life certainly was very slow and uneventful compared with the times we live in now. About once a month Mrs. Mitchell went to Tunbridge Wells to see her daughter Ada. She also sometimes saw her son Harold, who was a plumber. Mr. Mitchell, who was dead, had been a plumber too.

It was seven miles each way and she went in the carrier's van, which took nearly two hours to get there. Mrs. Mitchell's only newspaper was *The Kent and Sussex Courier*, which arrived once a week, and was called 'the Curryer'. Would she have been any wiser, I wonder, if her mind had been re-stocked every morning by doses of sensational journalism? As things were, she regaled us with popular fallacies and 'vulgar errors', and her mind was like the cupboard at the end of the nursery passage which she called her 'glory-hole'. In that dark cupboard she used to rummage among mysterious objects connected with her past history, and from the cupboard of her mind she produced such notions as would, she supposed, frighten us into growing up as well-behaved boys. But she had ruled over us ever since we could remember and we were quite fond of her, never doubting that everything she told us was true. She was, as it were, a sort of nursery Jehovah; she was the Old Testament, and my mother was the New Testament.

Much as we loved Mamsy, her personal influence was less powerful than Mrs. Mitchell's. But we had our own private mental territory, as all children have, and a very independent one it was. The fact that there were three of us enabled us to get on very comfortably without other children. My mother's attempts to introduce little friends were all failures. From the first we regarded these potential playmates with contempt or even hostility, and invariably ended by pulling their hair and tearing their clothes. When my mother gave a full-sized afternoon party for us we walked about together hand in hand, refusing to join in any games with our guests. Our only response was when we took charge of a fat little boy called Freddie, for whom we felt a special dislike, and shut him up in a cupboard. On festive occasions away from home we softened under the influence of Christmas trees, bran pies, and conjurors. (Do bran pies ever happen now, I wonder?) There was also our annual Servant's Party. We took a great interest in that. Dominated by Mrs. Mitchell, the Hall Party, as it was called, began at half-past seven, when my mother took us out to the studio in the garden to watch the dancing begin. When we arrived the men and women were standing on opposite sides of the room, extremely shy and completely silent. When my mother and Mrs. Mitchell had induced them to mix a bit, the local fiddler struck up with 'Sir Roger de Coverley' and the Hall Party was under way. The squeaky fiddler worked hard, but much of the music was supplied by the nursery hurdy-gurdy—an instrument known as the 'Ariston organ'—which played rather muffled tunes which passed for polkas and waltzes.

It occurs to me now that as no one in the room knew Greek, the word 'Ariston' was taken for granted as being the name of the organ's inventor. To me, I must admit, the name always seemed to suit the music, though I had no notion that it meant anything. Anyhow the dancing was much the slowest I have ever seen. Round and round the room they went, scarcely moving their feet at all, to the strains of 'Little Brown Jug' and other popular airs.

After about three hours they came indoors. I can remember looking out of the night-nursery window and seeing by the light of the moon a sedate procession of couples arm-in-arm, on their way to the servant's hall where goose and plum pudding awaited them. Later on they went back and kept it up till daybreak, and finished by singing 'Auld Lang Syne'.

One of my earliest literary compositions was an account of the Hall Party, in which I described the social embarrassment of a young traction-engine driver who sometimes passed our house and to whom we always waved——engine-driving being, of course, a much esteemed career. The genial driver always waved back at us and he became known as 'the stout young man'; and we insisted on his being invited to the party.

II

One memorable event had been our first visit to the Thornycroft Works at Chiswick. Battleships were built there—not 'ironclads', but torpedo-boats and destroyers—and the whole place belonged to Uncle John and Uncle Don. Uncle John, who was an engineering genius, designed the boats, and Uncle Don looked after everything else. (Uncle John was my mother's eldest brother John Thornycroft, and Uncle Don was John Donaldson who had married one of her sisters.) The noise of machinery and clanging hammers had appealed to us very much, and when we felt exuberant on wet days indoors we used to go into the bathroom and pretend to be 'the Works'. This, of course, consisted in making as much of a din as possible by hitting the copper bath with something hard until Mrs. Mitchell descended on us in her wrath.

In the summer of 1893 we went again to the Works. This time we saw the launch of the *Speedy* as we called her.

The *Speedy* was a torpedo-gunboat, and she was launched by Princess May, who was wearing a white dress and a large hat full of flowers. Looking rather shy and nervous, she smashed a bottle of champagne on the bow of *Speedy*, who thereupon slid smoothly into the Thames amid the huzzas of the spectators. I wonder what happened to her afterwards? Let us hope she did as well as Princess May, who became better known as Queen Mary.

*   *   *

In the spring of 1894 Grandmama Thornycroft came to live with us. Looking at a photograph taken at the time, I see her as I saw her then— sitting by a window in the drawing-room, dignified in the serene consolations of old age. One could not imagine her vexed or angry (though she once got rather agitated when we climbed to the top of the Wellingtonia in the garden). One could not imagine her as anything other than as she appears in the photograph, wearing a black silk gown with white ruffles and looking away into the past as though it were somewhere beyond the double windows (put in specially to preserve her from draughts) and gently remembering the years in which her beautiful long hands had been so active in modelling wax and clay.

For she had been the most distinguished sculptress of her time, both noble and natural in her art. Her benevolent voice, with a note of pathos in it, and her unvarying sweetness, made her seem an epitome of angelic old ladyhood. But one afternoon when Uncle John came to see her, I had a glimpse of her as she must have been when in the prime of life. I was watching them as they walked up and down the drawing-room. Leaning on his arm, she seemed to be re-traversing the past while they continued in long and lively conference, forgetful of their surroundings and aware only of the urgency of their talk. Uncle John himself was a remarkable looking man, with his ruddy face, absent-minded eyes, and greying red-gold hair and beard. But Grandmama's movements were majestic, and even then I discerned her as the honoured mother proudly reunited to her distinguished son. To be like that, I decided, was indeed to be most impressively grown-up. I also felt that it was needful that I should make efforts to emulate the importance they had arrived at—and were, so it seemed, still progressing toward—as they paced the parquet floor from end to end while Grandmama's voice went on and on—speaking, as I now realize, beyond and above her everyday self, and regaining, while her spirit burnt brightly like the leaping fire at the end of the room, something of the glorious vitality of her younger years. I, a child, somehow knew all this; and I remember it now, grateful for the pride in my mother's family with which the scene inspired me.

I, a child, knew that Grandmama Thornycroft was someone to be looked up to as well as loved. But I did not know, as I do now, that in addition to being a gracious and beautiful old lady in a white shawl, she was a woman of strong character and rich humanity whose favourite fireside reading was in *Hudibras* and *Tristram Shandy*.

My grandmother did one thing for me which made me feel very fond of her. For several years I had been deeply attached to a toy cow. Originally a solid cow on a wooden stand, she had gradually become a limp and flattened piece of leather. This had been caused by my keeping her under my pillow after her early detachment from the wooden stand. With sympathetic awareness of Moocow's importance, Grandmama stitched up her burst sides and inserted wash-leather patches, to my complete satisfaction. Moocow had, I suppose, become a sort of fetish. I used to converse with her when I was alone, and around her I created a dream existence. She ceased to be a toy cow, and

became a companionable character with whom
shared interesting adventures, in regions of escape
from my surroundings. (I called her 'she', but I
thought of her as neither one thing nor the other—
my idea about men and women being that they
dressed differently so as to show the difference; I
hadn't as yet consciously considered the question
of how bulls differed from cows.)

Moocow's friends and relations lived in a country inhabited by people called 'Mezenthrums'; I
used to talk to them down a small hole in the
cement between the blue and white Dutch tiles on
the bathroom wall. I gave them messages from
Moocow, visualizing them in a vague way as a
crowd of people among whom there were some
whom I gradually got to know quite well. (This
device was probably suggested by the speaking-
tube which went from outside the dining-room to
the lower regions.) I also used to unscrew one of
the brass knobs on my bedstead and by doing this
'get into another world' where anything I wished
for could happen in my mind. Mrs. Mitchell for-
bade me to do this because there was verdigris
under the knob, she said, and if you licked it you
would get poisoned. So knob-unscrewing became
a secret and doubly-attractive experiment. I had a
notion, too, that I might be able to do something
magical if I had a bar of platinum. My mother had

a platinum bracelet which I believed to be very valuable, and the word platinum suggested magical properties. The people in my other world were human but quite unlike anything I had seen or heard about; they were neither dream nor reality; I just invented them. My attachment to Moocow lasted until I was nearly nine; by then I had gradually discarded her as something a bit babyish for a boy of my age.

*   *   *

After the dismal wet summer of 1894 we began to be given hints that we must not be too hopeful about our father's recovery. I prayed persistently for him and consulted Moocow when in need of consolation, but there was a funereal feeling among us when Mrs. Mitchell took us to Eastbourne in November. Grandmama asked to be remembered to him, in a restrained and regretful sort of voice, when I was saying good-bye to her; sitting in her usual corner up on the sofa by the window, she gave me a sip of her port wine.

Being at Eastbourne was a forlorn experience. It had become merely a matter of our father wanting us to be near him for a few days. We used to sit in his room, but he wasn't allowed to talk much now, for he was very weak and his eyes looked enormous as he watched us from his bed. We weren't allowed to kiss him, for fear of catching consumption, and every day he seemed to be a little further away from our carefully subdued chatter.

One afternoon Mrs. Mitchell told us that we should find our other grandmama there. We didn't know much about our other grandmama, except that she and our mother had stopped being friendly several years ago. 'Pappy' had quarrelled with her too, but now she had come from Brighton to see him. She was standing by the bed, talking very fast in a foreign voice; when she turned and came toward us I saw that she was small and had rather a brown face. She was very lively and seemed kind and was delighted at seeing us, but she wasn't what we expected a grandmother to be like; she didn't look at all old and had a disconcerting way of laughing at what we said and did, when we weren't trying to be funny. She had brought a lot of flowers with her, red ones, which must have been camellias, and white ones which made the room smell of lilies, and were probably tuberoses. She wasn't grandly dressed, however, but looked rich in a quiet sort of way, and one felt that she could be very dignified if she wanted to. After asking us a lot of quick little questions without bothering to wait for an answer, she picked up a roll of paper which was on a table and showed us the printed pedigree of the Sassoon family. First of all she put her finger on a name at the top and said: 'Your great-grandfather.' Then she ran her finger down to the bottom of the list and said: 'Yourselves.' Sure enough, there we were, at the foot of the tree, and it was the first time I'd seen my own name in print.

From across the years it comes back to me, that picture of the sick-room, with dusk falling and 'Pappy's' face propped up on the pillows, and Grandmama Sassoon bending over us while her other son Joseph stood with his hands in his pockets, staring moodily out at the sunless seaside winter afternoon. And it comes back to me, that sense of being among strangers, with 'Pappy' being killed by that terrible cough, and the queer feeling that although this new grandmama was making such a fuss of us, it would make no difference if we never saw her again. I can see myself gazing at the Family Tree and wondering what all those other Sassoons were like, and how my great-grandfather had managed to produce so many of them. And I remember my miserable feeling that the only thing which mattered was that my mother ought to be there, and that these people were unfriendly to her who loved my father as they had never done and would have come to him with unquestioning forgiveness. Even Mrs. Mitchell was against her; for I knew, with a child's intuition, how she had helped to keep them apart.

*　　*　　*

The year '95 began with freezing cold weather which lasted for nearly two months. There was any amount of snow, and great was our excitement when the red-painted sledge was brought out of the stable barn, and my mother drove her two ponies tandem along the glossy rutted lanes with all three of us snuggling in beside her, and the big sheepskin rug drawn up to our chins and our woolly tam-o'-shanters pulled down to our noses. The bells jingled merrily as we went gliding crisply on until we arrived at the Furnace Pond, which was half a mile long and no one knew for certain how deep. Admiringly we watched 'Mamsy' put on her skates and strike confidently out across the black well-swept ice to join a group of local gentry who were either practising the outside edge or totteringly attempting to achieve it. She looked as free as a bird, skating away from all her worries to cut figures of eight with rosy-faced Captain Ruxton (a jocular crony of hers who had gone into the Army just too late for the Crimean War). They made a good pair as they were both short and compact. We only had one pair of skates at present, so while one of us wobbled up and down, trying to learn, the other two did a bit of erratic snow-sweeping until the food hamper was lugged out of the sledge and Captain Ruxton, brisk and jolly as the weather, made a roaring fire on the bank and boiled water in a large black kettle. Everyone's tea was laced with rum, and even we were allowed a spoonful in ours.

Later on, when the sun was getting low and it was time to be starting home, my mother drove the sledge across the pond in great style, and we felt that we had done something splendid.

But life wasn't all sledge-bells for my mother. The bitter cold weather was too much for Grandmama Thornycroft. At the end of January she was ill for a week and died very peacefully. We were told afterwards that toward the end her mind went back into the past and she talked as though she were living again in the times when she had been most happy. It was summer in her room while she lay there dying; perhaps she was back in Rome; she had spent the first years of her married life there, working at her art with Grandpapa, who was also a sculptor: he had died about ten years ago in this same house, from the effects of a sunstroke, which he had got by falling asleep under the skylight of his steam-launch, the *Water-Lily*.

I hoped that she had been back on the *Water-Lily* too, for my mother had often said how happy they all used to be together on the boat when she was a girl and they went up and down the Thames. The idea of Grandmama revisiting the past like that was very consoling and beautiful, especially as I did not doubt that it was only the beginning of a journey which would end in Heaven, where she would be eternally young and much happier than she'd ever been before.

During her last days we led a subdued life in the nursery; members of the family came and went and the doctor's carriage with its lamps like golden eyes used to wait outside the house in the middle of the night.

Grandmama's face was wonderfully still and peaceful when we saw her lying in her coffin in the drawing-room, surrounded by white lilies. But it was a relief when the hearse came and took her away and she went to London by train to be buried at Chiswick, almost near enough to the Thornycroft Works to hear the sound of the hammers—this having been her expressed wish. My mother told us that one of Queen Victoria's daughters had sent a wreath and a letter of condolence to the family. Poor old Grandmama, we said, as we laced up our boots and went out to build a snow fort on the lawn; and we wondered when we should be out in the sledge again, and how soon after the funeral 'Mamsy' would be able to skate.

*   *   *

It must have been soon after this that Mrs. Mitchell went off to Eastbourne for the day. She didn't tell us much when she returned. 'Pappy' was about the same and sent us his best love and a large box of preserved fruits, which Mrs. Mitchell doled out to us one at a time 'when we were good'. In the meantime we realized that she herself wouldn't be with us much longer, for it was obvious that we couldn't go on being children for ever. My elder brother had been ten last October; he was supposed to be rather delicate, but didn't show much sign of it. Mrs. Mitchell treated us as though we were all about seven, and still scrubbed our faces in the morning and shut us up in the cupboard when we displeased her. (The cupboard was a narrow box-room with one small window out of which one could see into the pump-yard if one stood on the top of a trunk).

Much though she interfered with our freedom, the idea of Mrs. Mitchell going away caused a feeling that some permanent safeguard was being removed. We shall never go out blackberrying with her again, I thought; and I saw the past as something cosy and familiar, where she was giving me a lump of sugar with a drop of camphorated oil on it when I had a cold. The future was like an empty room in which we had to begin all over again after a thorough spring-cleaning of our prolonged childhood. But at the same time I was aware that something had gone very wrong with Mrs. Mitchell's behaviour to my mother, toward whom she had become noticeably insolent after her visit to Eastbourne. (The explanation may have been that she had found out for certain that she was to be 'safely provided for' in my father's will.)

In the middle of March he died. Although I had been told that it was a happy release, I wondered how long I ought to go on crying about him, for I felt as if I should never stop. Mrs. Mitchell took my brothers to the funeral, which was at the Jewish Cemetery in London. I was too much upset to go. I felt desolate, because of so much happiness which could never happen now that he was dead; for he had made everything seem so promising when we were with him before he was ill. It was no consolation to assume that he had gone straight to Heaven, like Grandmama—entering by a different gate owing to his being buried in Hebrew instead of English.

What my brothers told me about the funeral

gave my misery a new lease of life. They returned tired and disconsolate, in their black suits, and the weather had been cold and gloomy; but that didn't explain the fact that the ceremony had frightened them. I gathered from what they said that something queer and gruesome had been done to 'Pappy' in his coffin. 'Two old men in funny-looking hats walked up and down saying jabber-jabber-jabber' was how my elder brother described the rabbis, in his first forlorn attempt to make the best of it. But the whole business had given them both a shock, because it was so strange to them. We knew that 'Pappy' had given up that sort of religion a long time ago, and I couldn't understand why he hadn't been buried in Brenchley churchyard, which had such nice big yew trees and the bells which we could hear across the fields on fine days. I didn't even know where the Jewish Cemetery was. They could only tell me that they had driven miles to get there with the blinds of the carriage pulled down. My elder brother said that there had been some rough-looking people watching the funeral; he had seen one of them taking flowers from a newly-made grave. It horrified me to think of poor 'Pappy' being buried in a place where people behaved like that. I saw it all in squalid clearness; the thought of Heaven was no help to me when those imagined sounds of outlandish lamentation were in my ears. I felt death in a new way now, and it seemed as though our father had been taken away from us by strangers. What my mother felt I need not try to revive. Being brave and unselfish she showed only her power to comfort us in our grief and perplexity. 'Pappy' had sent no message to her. Surely that must have been hard to bear.

*   *   *

At the end of March Mrs. Mitchell went away. I can remember going out into the garden after tea on her last day. Hearing the blackbirds scolding among the laurel bushes by the studio, I had that feeling, which we all know so well, of winter being over and the days really getting longer at last, and somehow it seemed to fit in with not having an old nurse to look after us any more. I wondered if Mrs. Mitchell would say good-bye to 'Mamsy' after being so rude to her yesterday. Anyhow, 'Pappy' had left her a hundred a year, so she was retiring in comfort. My brothers had gone down to 'The Build'; I could just see the fire they'd made, twinkling through the trees. But I didn't feel like joining them, so I did a bit of wool-gathering while sailing a couple of walnut-shell boats on the pigeon's bath in front of the studio. Though it was a chilly evening we all stayed out of doors till it was nearly dark, but no Mrs. Mitchell came to call us in, for she was busy packing up. When I returned to the nursery her 'glory hole' cupboard at the end of the passage was wide open and empty, and she was just taking her coloured photograph of the Toad Rock at Tunbridge Wells off the mantelpiece. When I asked if I could help her she didn't answer, and I felt sorry that she was going away so grumpy. Gazing rather wistfully at the Ariston organ and its pile of cardboard tunes on the shelf in the corner, I suddenly realized that she would never grind its handle again. Our nursery jollifications were all over. The Ariston, though I was incapable of formulating the thought, had become an emblem of those years during which she had extracted the well-known tunes from it.

In my eight-year-old way I must have been mindful of the accumulation of jokes and enjoyments which she had shared with us. For she had been a good nurse to us, in spite of her bad temper and old-fashioned ideas. And now she was going off in a 'growler' to Tunbridge Wells, late at night, to live with her daughter Ada, who had shown me how to play the Jew's harp and had given me quite a nice mouth-organ only last Christmas. She was going away for ever as if she had never done anything for us at all—as if there had never been a smell of fried sprats when we were having a treat for our tea, and as if she had never exclaimed 'Oh my stars and garters and Betty Martins!' when something astonished her.

Some time after we were all in bed, she came with her candle and cruised heavily about the room tidying up our clothes which we'd thrown on the floor. In a brooding sort of way she bent over us to say good-bye. Everything seemed rather queer that night. My head ached and my hands and feet were as if they were a long way off. We should see her again in the summer, I thought, as she closed the door and went creaking along the passage for the last time.

III

Not long before Mrs. Mitchell went away, an old friend of my mother's called Miss Batty had come to spend a few months with us. She wasn't a governess, but we were going to do lessons with her until a suitable tutor had been found. Hitherto our education had been elementary and irregular; and even now it was to be a long time before I had any more lessons, for on the night of Mrs. Mitchell's departure I developed pneumonia. It must have come on very suddenly; I remember waking up in the middle of the night to find my mother and Ellen Batty leaning over me and listening to my chest; after that I became too ill to know what was happening, and was only just aware of the kind, bearded face of Doctor Neild looking down at me: my mother and Ellen Batty became an indistinguishable presence with a feeding bottle. I was told afterwards that my temperature had been 105 and

that I had been delirious, which I felt rather proud
of. There was no doubt that having pneumonia
had been a stupendous experience; it was almost
like being outside the world altogether, or at any
rate like being in a world of dream-work so terrific
that I afterwards thought of it as a sort of super-
natural revelation. Those vague multitudes under
enormous flame-lit arches—what could they have
been if they were not something to do with death?
Even now I can recover my awed sensation of
having been away from life, of having had a glimpse
of something for which I had no words. Anyhow,
nights and days had been all the same for me, until
one morning I awoke and saw the April sunshine
flooding into my room and knew that I had returned safely from those borderlands.

Getting well again was very enjoyable at first. I
felt that it was the only time I'd ever had a nice
long holiday from everyday life. But I very soon
fell into a booby-trap which life had arranged for
me in the following way.

Ellen Batty, who liked mysteries, had got it into
her head that there was some connexion between
Mrs. Mitchell and my pneumonia, and had imbued my mother with the same suspicion. Mrs.
Mitchell had been on bad terms with them both
at the end of her time; she had been strongly suspected of listening outside the drawing-room door

in the evenings, which had caused them to converse in not very fluent French. Unable to resist the temptation to make a good story out of it, I supported the idea that I had caught sight of Mrs. Mitchell doing something to my sheets with a sponge. It seems odd that they managed to believe that slightly damped sheets could cause immediate pneumonia; but they did, and after my first gratification at having caused such a stir I began to feel guilty and remorseful.

I knew that every good little boy had a conscience, which was a contrivance attached to him by the Almighty, like the lamp of a safety bicycle, to be used in the dark. Mine had now become both active and uneasy, not so much because I had maligned Mrs. Mitchell as from fear of being punished for it by God. Mrs. Mitchell herself had often warned me that one really wicked deed sent a person to hell; my conscience now told me that unless I could undo this sin of mine I should go there for a dead certainty. Supposing I told my mother that I wasn't sure, after all, that I hadn't been quite mistaken about what I'd told her. Would that do any good, I wondered. No, replied my conscience, adding a reminder that God could see through walls and ceilings and wasn't to be deceived. I wasn't even certain that He really would forgive me if I confessed that I'd invented the whole story about Mrs. Mitchell and the sponge. The more I worried about it the surer I was that hell-fire was waiting for me. And when I did contrive to get through a day without remembering it, I had horrible dreams in which I was in hell and had been about to be pushed into the fiery furnace when I woke to see the friendly flicker of the night-light burning low in its little dish. Our Saviour was no use to me now; for I had put myself beyond his power to save me, and Satan would be there waiting for me as soon as I was dead. Miserably I resigned myself to everlasting perdition; all I could do was to put it off as long as possible by living to be about a hundred.

Meanwhile I continued my career as an interesting invalid in the best bedroom with the washbasin which had the big blue fish on it. At the beginning of May I was still in bed and had very little strength in me, but I was well enough to enjoy games of Halma and Beggar-my-neighbour with my brothers, who had never been so respectful to me before, though I had to remind them occasionally that I had very nearly died a few weeks ago and must be treated as such. My younger brother was very anxious to do things for me, and lent me a Stag Beetle which he had caught in the pump-yard, just outside the pantry window. (He kept it in the cage of a former canary of ours which had been killed by the cat.) Ellen Batty was my devoted slave. She was an old hand at keeping children amused and had an everlasting stock of stories. She could make almost anything into a story, but her best ones were about India.

A lot of her relations had been out there, and her mind was full of things which she had once heard from colonels and judges, whose children had so often begged her to tell them just one more story; meanwhile their parents were far away, looking after the British Empire. Her most popular performance with us was an interminable improvisation about a punkah-wallah, a ludicrous but likeable character whose exciting adventures were caused by diabolic tribesmen who crawled around the bungalow by night intending to murder the sahibs for whom he worked the punkah. These lithe ruffians were addicted to drinking arrack and bhang—names which created an atmosphere of evil-doing. In spite of his many absurd mistakes, the punkah-wallah always emerged heroic and virtuous.

While I was getting over my illness she told me a lot of stories from the Old Testament. She made even these sound quite new and exciting, in spite of doing it in a rather reverent voice. I had always liked hearing about the twelve tribes and could imagine it all without thinking of the Bible illustrations I'd looked at. 'They all seem to have the right names,' I remarked to Batty, though I couldn't explain exactly what I meant. 'Abraham couldn't have been called Elijah, could he? If he had been he wouldn't have had that long grey beard.' I had great respect and affection for Abraham, and I admired Elijah for calling down curses on those beastly priests of Baal. It gave me vague satisfaction merely to hear some of the names spoken. The word Pharaoh, for instance, suggested someone with a very beautiful voice standing alone at the top of a lot of stone steps with the evening star shining above him. Solomon, on the other hand, always appeared to be talking to a large buzzing crowd, possibly because I had heard that he had a million wives. Such names were like vanilla, which smelt the same as it sounded.

We also rambled about in the history of England. I assumed that the world had begun with the Bible, so it was all plain sailing till one got to the end of B.C. Between the Crucifixion and Alfred the Great there didn't seem much to get hold of. I became inattentive when Batty talked about the Romans conquering Kent. The Romans suggested Latin, which 'Mamsy' had tried to teach me last winter; so far it only meant *Mensa*, a table on which one was writing it down. I took more interest in the Danes, who had red hair, like the Thornycrofts—a thing that made them more real than the Romans. The Danes had done a lot of damage, of course, but Alfred ('Pappy's' name was Alfred, by the way) had converted them into being almost the same as the English, so after that they were all right. William Rufus being shot by an arrow and Henry the Somethingth dying of eating too many lampreys were easy enough to remember, and then came Richard Cœur de Lion, who was in Batty's opinion a compendium of noble qualities. She preferred to gloze over the bad people in the history book, and made the best of the doubtful ones. I took a special interest in Queen Elizabeth because, apart from her famousness, there was a brass-faced clock on our dining-room wall which everyone said had been made in her reign, and Time as I reckoned it seemed somehow to have started when its lead weights began to swing and it struck its first hour. (It didn't measure the minutes.) Most of the people in history seemed much more alive when one got to Queen Elizabeth. There was Shakespeare by then, and Sir Philip Sidney (whose house at Penshurst was only about ten miles away from us).

Ellen Batty gave me an idea of the world which was quite different from Mrs. Mitchell's. She had suspected almost everybody of being either sly or wicked; in her world people only behaved well because they were afraid of being sent to prison, and she only trusted them as far as she could see them. Batty's world was divided into very good people and hopelessly bad ones. The bad ones came in useful in her stories, when she wanted to make one's flesh creep, and the good ones were sometimes almost too good to be quite believable. All the others would turn out well in the end, she thought; God always forgave them if they really repented, even at the last moment. He wanted little boys like myself to grow up into splendid soldiers who won the Victoria Cross, or gallant sailors who got the Albert Medal for saving someone from drowning or being eaten by sharks, or else missionaries who taught black men—and even cannibals—to believe in Jesus and read the Scriptures. She used to read me a book called *Deeds that Won the Empire*. To be like General Gordon was about the best thing one could do, she suggested. My Uncle Hamo had made a statue of him which was in Trafalgar Square; there was a photograph of it hanging above the mantelpiece in the room where I was now lying in bed. The sun had gone down but I could see the tops of the red may trees in bloom below the open window while Batty was telling me how Gordon had been heroically killed by the dervishes at Khartoum. Being a hero nearly always meant getting killed, it seemed, but I supposed that the glory made it

worth while. And God was waiting with His blessing on the other side of the grave. Waiting; but
not for me, I suddenly remembered. Not for me,
who hadn't thought it worth while to say my
prayers for the last few weeks, and could do nothing to get my trespasses forgiven. At any rate I
could burst into tears and tell Batty all about it,
and be only too glad to believe that everything
would be all right now that Mrs. Mitchell wasn't
blamed any more for my pneumonia.

Naturally I felt more relieved than I could say;
for I was reprieved from being sent to hell even if
I wasn't yet sure of going to Heaven. Nothing
would ever be said about it again, Batty assured
me, her eyes looking very grave and gentle.

Dear Ellen Batty, with her wide mouth and
rather sallow face which wrinkled and puckered
like a tomato under her black hair that was
streaked with white; who always dressed in brown
and wore queer shapeless hats that got on one
side, whose portmanteau key usually got lost on
the journey, and who did everything one asked her,
even to allowing one to put her Indian bead neck-
laces in the pigeon's bath so as to find out what
they looked like in water. I see her, vague and
unpractical and indefatigable, with her little white
fox-terrier Spider, who had such a sweet nature
and never chased cats. If Heaven can be made real

by trusting in it, hers was never far away, and it was full of happy children, some of whom had brown skins when they were on earth, but now they all had blue eyes and golden hair. Even Spider would go to Heaven, she told me, and Peter, our kitchen cat, though he *was* so deceitful and had often stolen things from the larder. 'Do canaries go to Heaven?' I asked. Yes, they did, she replied, and no one kept them in cages up there. After that she put her hands on my forehead to draw the headache away, and then she sent me to sleep with one of her most soothing stories.

*   *   *

When the warmer weather began, a little tent was put up for me on the lawn. Every morning I was carried downstairs on a stretcher to spend the day in my tent. My mother considered it out of the question for me to walk, and as I enjoyed being carried and still felt rather fragile I allowed this precaution to continue as long as I could keep it up.

To be out of doors again at that time of year was indeed like coming back to life. But it was more than that, for illness had made my perceptions detached and sensitive. I know how memory idealizes things; but I think, all the same, that this was my first conscious experience of exquisite enjoyment. The tent gave me a feeling of independence and security as I lay there and listened to a pattering shower or gazed at wisps and shoals of silvery cloud on mornings when the air was heavenly fresh and even the sky looked innocent—mornings when I was alone and the dew not yet off the grass in the undiminished shadows of that garden world.

I was beginning to discover that solitude could quicken my awareness of aspects within me and around me. My pneumonia had revealed that I had a mind with which I liked to be alone. My brothers had been told not to disturb me; but when they did, I could hear without envying them that they'd made a new palisade round 'The Build' with some stakes which the wood-cutters had left lying about in the wood last winter. Let them slide down the banisters as much as they pleased or send Peter the cat up and down in the dining-room lift. I was quite contented to be where I was. It was enjoyable, too, to know that they were doing arithmetic with Batty up in the nursery (now called the schoolroom) or to hear one of them squeaking on his fiddle in the drawing-room. I wanted to remain an invalid indefinitely, feeling almost as if I were invisible till 'Mamsy' came out with my meals or my beaten-up egg in milk in the middle of the morning which Doctor Neild had ordered me.

I liked to hear the sounds of life going on around me—the jays (jolly mischievous jays they were) squawking down among the green-peas, and the gruff voices of the gardeners at their work. There was the rumble of the wheelbarrow being trundled down a path; and later on, in June, when they were mowing the long grass in the orchard, the sound of a scythe being sharpened on a stone. Not much happened. It was all quite peaceful and remote from any obligation to exert oneself. At about three o'clock I would hear the horses come in at the front gate; for a few minutes they would stamp and snort, and then there would be the murmur of my mother's voice while she mounted to start out for a sauntering ride along the shady lanes with our groom Richardson, who was going to teach me to jump when I was well again, though I didn't feel much like tumbling off a pony at present. On the high tiled roof of the studio the cosy white pigeons cooed or fluttered down to have a drink and peck up maize, and I knew that I was safe with my daydreams for another hour or two.

I was fond of sniffing a little scent phial which I had borrowed from my mother. The bottle was filigreed with dusty gold and had formerly contained attar of roses, which I believed to be worth a guinea a drop. It was empty now, but a faint aroma remained. The phial had been given to her long ago by my father, and I unconsciously made it a symbol of the time when they had been happy together. I supposed it to have come from Persia, where my ancestors had lived, so it seemed a sort of essence of my father's oriental extraction.

Thus I lay, reposefully reviving in convalescent quietude, aware—and yet unaware—of the blue evening distance of the Weald beyond the tree-tops and the green tangles of our terraced untidy garden; hearing—but not enphrasing—the songs of birds, and ignorant of the world toward which the trains went along the valley. There it all was—looked at by the uncomparing eyes of a child whose mind had so little in it to remember that the landscape was like life, empty as yet and almost unlearned. In a crab-apple tree close to my tent there hung a small Aeolian harp that lent to the light summer breezes a local euphony which swelled and faded to a melodious murmur. The sound was like poetry; for even then poetry could just stir my mind—as though it were some living and yet mysterious spirit—touching me to a blurred and uncontrolled chord of ecstasy.

IV

By the middle of July I had rather reluctantly given up being an invalid. Life became ordinary-looking again, and the reveries I had enjoyed in my tent were almost forgotten in everyday doings with my brothers. Only the idea that I wanted to write poems remained at the back of my mind.

There was something else to look forward to, however, for in August we were all going to the Isle of Wight to stay with Uncle John and Aunt Blanche, who had a lovely big house at Bembridge, in those days a quiet and unspoilt place. When we got there we had a glorious time with our grown-up girl cousins and their schoolboy brother Tom, who had a little sailing boat of his own and had built himself a crow's nest at the top of a lime tree and knew all about bird's eggs. There was a bathing cove which was practically private. There we began to learn swimming while our cheerful cousins dived into the sparkling blue sea as though nothing could come between them and success. They laughed and talked in rather high-pitched voices and had hair which caught its colour from the sunshine that had freckled their open-air faces. They took photographs, too, which came out splendidly, and it was all rather like a clear photograph taken in fine weather. I went out butterflying with one of them, and was dumb with admiration at the way she chased about with her large green net; and the skill with which she had set her specimens made me feel a bit depressed about my own untidy little collection at home.

Uncle John was the only member of the family who didn't talk much. At meals he was silent and absent-minded; but he, of course, was a famous naval engineer. He had 'the calculating faculty', my mother told me, which meant that he could calculate all sorts of sums about boat-building in his head and always get the answer right.

'Uncle John invented the tubular boiler' was the description I had learnt to attach to him, but he seemed to spend most of his time cutting roses or pulling up weeds; when I passed him he would look up, pink-faced and fluffy-bearded, smile seraphically, and stoop again to his gardening.

From our happy holiday in this Thornycroft Elysium we went home to start improving our minds, for my mother had at last engaged a tutor. His name was Jas. A. Moon. He was a retired elementary schoolmaster who had recently arrived to live on the village green, next door to the blacksmith. It had been a case of natural selection, since, as far as I can remember, there had been no other candidate for the post. But the selection had been a wise one, for Mr. Moon was just the sort of tutor we wanted.

Affectionately nicknamed 'Moony', he was one of the mildest of men. Nobody could have been more like an indulgent tutor and less like a stern taskmaster. Patient, methodical, and unhurrying, he taught us grammar, simple arithmetic, a little Latin, some rather dimly defined geography, and the conventional outline of English history. Most of our exercises were done on slates, but we were promoted to pens, ink, and paper for dictation, which he did with a magisterial air.

> 'Delaney sends a silver stand-dish
> When I no more my pen can brandish'

he enunciated, with emphatic deliberation. I didn't inquire who Delaney was, and no explanation was offered about the 'stand-dish', but the couplet brings me a very distinct picture of Mr. Moon with his silver hair and straggling moustache—a tall, tired, stooping man, who never spoke fast and always wore the same black tail-coat. He was a teetotaller too; he told us that he had taken the blue ribbon as a youth and had never regretted it.

I see him, chalking the dates of famous battles on the blackboard, or writing in his careful slanting characters the names of certain remote but important rivers—the Dnieper, the Dniester, the Volga, the Elbe, and the Danube, and explaining exactly where their watersheds were; even now I visualize a watershed as a small wooden building on the top of a mountain.

Although we were considered rather unmanageable boys I don't think we caused Mr. Moon much trouble. His manner was meekly authoritative, but we obeyed him and took pains over our lessons because we were fond of him. Our serious studies were done in the morning. Mr. Moon (whose false teeth were an object of sympathetic interest) remained for luncheon, at which my mother took charge of our table manners, not always successfully. Afterwards we filled in an hour with something easy like Natural History or being read aloud to from Lamb's *Tales from Shakespeare* and *Robinson Crusoe* (whom we much preferred). We also did a bit of amateur carpentering—Mr. Moon taking off his coat for it. My brothers were more interested in this than I was. And then, if the weather was fine, we played about in the gar-

den, while Mr. Moon, somewhere in the offing
in his semi-clerical hat, allowed us to do as we
liked. And we took it in turns to go for a ride. Tom
Richardson, the groom, led the pony, listening to
my chatter with an imperturbable twinkle in his
good-looking face. Ever since I could remember,
Richardson had been part of the world as I knew
it. He was still in his twenties and had recently
married Grandmama's maid Emma. Discreet and
yet full of good jokes, he did everything in a jaun-
tily stylish way which made him a paragon in my
estimation, both then and ever afterwards. When
summer came round again, he and Mr. Moon used
to play cricket with us in the paddock below the
studio. Richardson was captain of the village team
and a dashing left-hand bat on those bumpy local
wickets. Mr. Moon's lobs were like himself, in-
offensive but accurate. They were tempting de-
liveries—too tempting for Tom to resist, and more
than once he hit Mr. Moon's bowling over the
studio.

By the summer of 1896, however, my mother
must sometimes have felt that she needed more
than Mr. Moon to control the clamour which went
on when he wasn't there. Her only effective ally in
preventing us from turning the whole house into a
bear-garden was Emily Eyles, who was nominally
the parlour-maid. Her duties would have been quite

simple if the parlour had contained no one but
my mother and her occasional visitors, with whom
Emily was a great favourite owing to her innocent
blue eyes and fair hair. She was the daughter of a
blacksmith at Brightling (a Sussex village which
we enjoyed hearing about) and had evidently in-
herited some of her father's fortitude, since the
more noise we made the more she seemed able to
endure. When we felt like sitting still in the evening
she used to read to us from our favourite books,
among which were *The Coral Island*, *Tom Sawyer*,
Round the World in Eighty Days, and *Black Beauty*;
there was also *Treasure Island*, of course; and we
had a somewhat surprising fondness for *The Diary
of a Nobody*—anyhow we showed surprisingly good
taste in realizing its excellence. Emily showed the
softer side of her nature in her partiality for a book
called *Golden Horseshoes* which someone had sent
us at Christmas. After the first reading I rejected
it as too sugary and prettified, but for Emily it was
a romantic dream. The story was about a young
knight, of whom I remember nothing except that
his impoverished lady mother gave him a purse of
gold rose nobles when he rode away to seek his
fortune, returning in the last chapter with a beautiful and high-born bride. We used to make fun of
Emily for being so wrapped up in *Golden Horseshoes*. We couldn't understand why people made

such a fuss about falling in love. Meanwhile she had little enough time for that sort of thing. I remember with gratitude how hard she worked for us and how gaily she did it. Mending torn clothes, tying up cut fingers, cleaning out the parrot's cage, and helping to find the cricket ball when it was lost in the sweet-briar hedge—these were only a few of Emily's extra duties.

My mother, had she been free to do so, would have spent several hours a day in the studio, for she had been a successful artist both before she was married and for a few years afterwards. Even now there were some large unfinished canvases in the studio which showed by their vigorous design how she had begun them with creative energy and had failed to complete them because there were so many other demands on her time and vitality.

Since Mr. Moon took us in hand she had been able to work more regularly, and she was now painting a portrait of Bessie Marchant in a white dress with some dark red roses in her hands. Bessie and her sister May were the daughters of our local Squire. They lived in a fine old Queen Anne house which overlooked the village green, and their family had been there for nearly two hundred years. Young, tall, and exuberant, May and Bessie often brought their joyous vitality to refresh my mother. They were like Juno and Ceres, she used to say, for May was fair, like a cornfield, while Bessie was dark, and had the quality of a damask rose. In character, too, they were well contrasted. May was practical minded, and had a glance which reproved me into better behaviour, rather as if one were in church, without the awkward holy feeling. She was kind-hearted and jocular, but one felt that she wasn't going to have any nonsense. She was good at golf—which was a more conspicuous accomplishment among ladies then—and was always ready to be bowled at by her cricketing brothers, one of whom was in my estimation world famous, for he had been captain of Cambridge and was now captain of Kent.

Bessie, on the other hand, was adorably tolerant. She always laughed, however outrageously we behaved. Impulsive and emotional, she made me feel that mistakes were easily forgiven because she made them herself. In her serious and romantic moods she practised her violin and read poetry; but she was as good as May at finding bird's nests and told amusing stories about the cottagers, imitating their way of talking.

Sometimes I was allowed to walk home with them, by my favourite footpath across the fields, with Bessie calling wildly to her yellow Irish terrier Shandy (whose full name was Shandygaff) when he, as usual, had vanished in search of a rabbit. I see her showing me a robin's nest in the hedge-bank, just before we crossed the lane and passed the old orchard and the farm buildings behind their house. And then we came into the courtyard, where the gilded stable clock was striking the hour and their brother Dick was giving his falcons some raw meat while his golden setter sat watching him; and the evening sunshine was on it all—as it is now in my mind, at the memory of those young voices in that dawdling homespun world of long ago.

In those days people who lived quietly in the country were much more dependent on their neighbours than they are now. My mother used to say that most of hers were like part of the land-scape; they never went away, and some of the ladies were rather 'hen-like' though otherwise estimable. So when she felt herself, as she said, 'becoming an absolute cabbage', she used to ride over to stay a night with Florence Bramwell, who lived about twenty miles away and was more in touch with the London dinner-party world than May and Bessie.

Florence Bramwell, whom she had known since they were girls together, was a lively and even brilliant talker. 'Really, some of her epigrams are almost as good as Meredith's,' I can imagine my mother saying to Bessie when she brought back *Diana of the Crossways* (which she had borrowed months ago and had ploughed through with difficulty). Anyhow Florence Bramwell was an antidote to dullness and an affectionate friend. I enjoy the thought of my mother and Tom Richardson jogging along the dusty road to Edenbridge on some sleepy summer afternoon in the middle '90's. The idea of that twenty miles being a long way is an attractive one, though in those days distance was, of course, no advantage. When Florence Bramwell came over to see us she arrived by train. She left me with a fixed idea that all brilliant women had rather bright red hair and looked at one through spectacles on the end of a tortoise-shell stick. My mother's hair had been Venetian red when she was younger, but my father had made her cut it quite short before I could remember, and it had lost a good deal of its colour now. She, however, couldn't be described as a brilliant talker in the usual sense of the words. But she had spontaneous and original phrases for the most ordinary matters, and her downright opinions were the delight of all who knew her. Time teaches one to admire such people, who refuse to pull a long face however deeply life may have hurt them, and whose cheerfulness is born of courage as well as being the outcome of their abundant aliveness.

During the winter of 1896 she made one of her efforts to enliven the neighbourhood by enlisting some of the local ladies in a poetry society. Essays were to be written, and were to be read aloud and discussed in our drawing-room.

The subject chosen for their inaugural essays was Shelley. The afternoon of the first meeting was wet and windy, so my brothers and I, feeling idle and mischievous, decided to hear what happened. At one end of the drawing-room there was ornamental woodwork which formed canopies on each side of the fireplace. By climbing the slender pillars which upheld one of these canopies we could get into a sort of loft about three feet high. One of the bars was removable and we could just squeeze through after a difficult climb which didn't improve the cream-coloured paint. Soon afterwards my mother, who had been putting on her mauve tea-gown, bustled in, stirred the fire, rearranged the chairs, and turned up the oil-lamps; she accompanied these activities with the 'Keel Row', rendered half-audibly in something between a hum and a whistle, as was her habit when preoccupied with her painting or putting flowers in water.

Owing to the frightful weather only about ten of the members turned up. I could just see the top of Miss Woodgate's tweed hat, but it wasn't safe to peep under the little curtain, and after watching them arrive we had to be content with listening. Two of the vicar's daughters had come carrying sheets of foolscap, and Mrs. Ruxton had something, which looked like an essay, sticking out of her untidy reticule, but several of the others confessed that they had been unable to collect their ideas about Shelley on paper. The ice was broken by Bessie, who began bashfully but gave quite a respectable performance, though a bit gushing about 'The Ode to the West Wind' (which sounded as if it were doing its best to blow the roof off our house). Her general conclusion seemed to be that Shelley was so inspired and wonderful that one couldn't find words to describe the feeling he gave one.

Then Miss Martin, who seldom spoke, but nodded her head like a mandarin and was reputed to be a great reader of solid literature—Miss Martin, who was gouty but had braved the bad weather, announced that, in the absence of her essay, she proposed to read them *Adonais*. Funereal solemnity prevailed while she did so in most lugubrious tones. *Adonais* contains almost five hundred lines and Miss Martin droned them out so slowly that the poem became a veritable dirge.

Would she never finish? I wondered, for the loft was very dusty, and sooner or later one of us was dead certain to sneeze.

'Who mourns for Adonais? O come forth,
   Fond wretch! . . .'

These lines might well have been addressed to the
loft. Anyhow they were a signal for one of us to
emit an irrepressible 'Tishoo' which caused a
prompt disclosure of our participation in the proceedings of the poetry society. Giggling, grimy,
and incorrigible, we climbed down to be ejected
from the room amid exclamations of 'Little
wretches!' No doubt they all laughed when we
were safely outside, and even pious Miss Martin
may have permitted herself a sepulchral chuckle
as they adjourned for tea and crumpets in the
dining-room. There was, I think, only one more
meeting—a Coleridge occasion, at which Miss
Martin read *The Ancient Mariner*. After that my
mother allowed the poetry society to lapse.

Her next attempt to redeem the district from
dullness was far more successful. At that time
tableaux vivants were in fashion, and she became
very busy about producing some. For several weeks
little else was talked about except 'The Tablows',
as we called them. My mother designed dresses
and painted bits of scenery, Emily Eyles stitched
for all she was worth, Donaldson nieces were sent
for from London to supplement May and Bessie
and other local young people, and sedate gentle-

men were called in to impersonate such characters as the dozing father in *Two's Company, Three's None*, or *She Stoops to Conquer*. When the eventful evening arrived we were all infused with the dressing-up feeling which enables human beings to escape from themselves. A small stage in the dining-room limited my mother's energetic ideas, but the heavy red curtains which shut off that end of the room were a help, though the foot-lights were only candles, aided in special effects by a sort of magic-lantern, worked by the Tonbridge photographer from where the Sheraton sideboard stood in everyday life (with the cat's dinner plate underneath it). But everyone considered it a wonderful entertainment, and the long waits between 'Tablows' only made the audience feel that something wonderful was being prepared. When my own turn drew near I began to feel nervous, though all I had to do was to hold the hand of a cousin from Chiswick and think of myself as Henry the Sixth at the age of ten. The episode was called 'Queen Margaret and the Robbers'. I wore red shoes with long twiddly toes to them. We were supposed to be in a forest during the Wars of the Roses, and I had to remember to keep quite still even if my nose started tickling.

The most exciting one was 'Bluebeard's Wives', which made me feel almost as if I were there.

Several of the wives were lying about murdered and there was jam for blood. There was a sort of stillness about it which horrified and enthralled my imagination. My younger brother thought it a mistake not to have made use of the studio skeleton, which had been acquired for artistic purposes and lived in a box like a coffin. I rebuked him, saying that the wives had only just been killed, and clinched it by reminding him that the skeleton (which we often used for scaring visitors with) was a Chinaman and couldn't have been one of Bluebeard's wives. The final tableau was *A Midsummer Night's Dream*, in which the whole company was crowded on to the stage. I was Mustard Seed, sitting on a painted canvas toadstool. There were dozens of twinkling glass dewdrops hanging from a cobweb which was the background. I wished it could have lasted longer, though I knew it was only a 'Tablow' and the dewdrops only crystal blobs off a chandelier. 'Tablows' seemed to me a perfect way of spending one's time, and I tried to store up as much of it as I could inside me when I went to bed. How lovely Bessie had looked in 'Drink to Me Only With Thine Eyes'—standing there rather shyly in her hooped pink dress with a gallant wooer on one knee before her.

Lovely indeed, as I remember her now, so immensely remote from to-day, when all those

people in fancy dresses are forty years older or
vanished for ever, and our *tableaux vivants*, if they
could be seen again, would be ridiculed as clumsy
improvisations, lacking even the aid of incidental
music.

A few months afterwards my mother followed
up her success with a second performance, which
took place in the studio and was an improvement
on the previous one. There were, of course, the
usual Royal Academy picture subjects, such as
'Two Strings to her Bow'. But the one I remember most clearly was called 'The Artist's Dream'.
It was in two scenes. In the first the artist was sitting in profound meditation before an empty canvas on an easel, thinking about his unpainted
masterpiece and also wanting to be happier and
less lonely. When the curtains were drawn back a
second time he had fallen asleep and was in obscurity. From the balcony above the studio the
photographer's lantern cast its light on the figures
which represented the artist's dream, while from
behind the stage my mother threw down some
gold dust which added to the visionary effect. A
girl with an aureole of fair hair and angel's wings
was standing with my younger brother, a beautiful
dark child also in white. He looked as if he really
was an angel, and her face seemed timeless in a
serenity that could never be altered. Gazing at

83

those seraphic forms in the snowstorm of slowly descending motes of gold, I could only feel that I had never seen anything more lovely. I did not know how sadly true to life and time it was—that entrancing illusion of perpetual innocence.

*   *   *

But I have been progressing too rapidly and must go back to the spring of 1896, which we made unforgettable by learning to bicycle. At first my mother opposed this ambition of ours, but we retaliated by taking to the road in Grandmama's old Bath chair. Starting from outside the front gate we could go nearly a mile down the hill, which was steep and had two sharp corners to make it exciting. Again and again we made the journey (after Mr. Moon had gone home), trying to break the record for how far we could get on the gentle gradient which ended at the crossroads where the oak railings of the old Pound still stood on an island of turf. My mother very soon decided that bicycling would be less dangerous, for bicycles had brakes, and people had begun to make remarks about the way we whizzed past them, steering erratically, as they toiled up the hill in their carriages. So a bicycle was bought and Tom Richardson, who had ridden one of the old high ones which you had to jump off when you wanted to dismount, soon helped us through our wobblings, and then three more machines were hired and we went for regular rides with Emily Eyles, who was timid but had learnt quite quickly.

But after a few weeks of exhilarating spins in every possible direction I developed mysterious pains in one of my hip joints, and Doctor Neild, who feared that I was outgrowing my strength, prescribed no more bicycling and a minimum of walking. This led to a second period of lying out on the lawn and feeling poetical. For several weeks I made the most of having a bad hip and enjoyed my inactivity until a craving for cricket put me on my feet again.

I now vaguely believed that I was going to be a poet, and had taken to reading Longfellow, Shelley, and Tennyson. I was rather secretive about it, feeling that poetry was a thing I wanted to keep to myself. I still loved to listen to my mother reading *The Water Babies*, which had been the favourite book of my childhood; but when she got to 'Clear and Cool' I wished she would leave it out; I preferred to be alone with it, for it was the most satisfying poem I had ever experienced. I had opened Shelley at random and the first few lines of *Queen Mab* had made me eager to read some more.

'How wonderful is Death,
   Death and his brother Sleep!'

I soon found the rest of the poem impossible, but
those lines remained in my head like a refrain. I
had a tendency to expect all the best poetry to be
gloomy, or at any rate solemn. Shelley was obviously a great poet because he wrote such a lot
about mountains. He didn't make me see anything
at all clearly, but when I chanced on lines like

'Therefore the names of Demon, Ghost, and
   Heaven,
Remain the records of their vain endeavour——'

I felt as if I were being carried away by him into
some tremendous mystery; there was a photograph
in the studio which gave me the same sensation;
my mother told me it was 'Tintoretto's Last
Judgement'.

Tennyson, on the other hand, made me see
everything he wrote quite distinctly, and I was
spellbound by his words and cadences. 'The Lady
of Shalott' was my idea of absolute perfection.
With Shelley one never knew where one was, but
in the 'Lady of Shalott' I did know, because my
mother and Ellen Batty had told me all about King
Arthur and his Round Table long ago. Lying in
bed I could imagine that it was a boat and float

down to 'many-towered Camelot' quite comfortably. I didn't try to think how it was done or what it was all about; I was in a world of exquisite romance, seeing (as I afterwards found out) a series of sweetly lighted Praeraphaelite pictures. Unconsciously I surrendered to the idea of seeing life reflected in a magic mirror, never suspecting that the moral of the poem was a warning to people who turn away from wholesome realities.

I too would some day write like Tennyson, I dreamed. I would break the spell which so far had prevented me from putting my wordless ecstasies into poetry. Had not Ellen Batty told me, after scrutinizing the lines of my hand, that I was to become a poet? And Batty was supposed to be awfully good at palmistry.

Later on in the summer I got to know the realities of a river which went flowing down—not to Camelot but to Maidstone. This was, of course, the River Medway. My mother having resolved to get us taught swimming, we made a weekly expedition to Wateringbury.

It always seemed to be a grey and gusty afternoon when we got out at Wateringbury station. Pretending to be more brisk and cheerful than we really felt, we made our way to Ted Avery's landing stage, where boats could be hired, carrying the picnic-basket and our bathing togs. Ted Avery was a hardy and jocular man in a blue jersey, but the River Medway smelt of mud and its bank felt shivery and unfriendly when I was lowering myself into the water to be played like a fish on the rope and pole apparatus for teaching people how to swim. 'Think of the way frogs do it,' Ted Avery advised me from above; but the water was going up my nose and I didn't want to be like a frog. I wanted to be like Tennyson.

Meanwhile my mother, who was a splendid swimmer, had dived in and was disporting herself as though the Medway were the nicest thing she'd ever been in, treading the water and telling me how to float on my back, until Emily Eyles emerged from behind an adjacent cow-shed to undergo similar instruction. Emily, who disliked the Medway as much as I did, never succeeded in learning at all. Afterwards we went in a boat and practised rowing, but the best thing in the afternoon was making a fire and boiling the kettle under an old willow.

One morning my mother bustled into the school-room and put an end to our lessons by announcing that a message had arrived inviting us all to go out in Mr. Arnold's steam-launch. Mr. Arnold lived about four miles away. He was our corn-merchant and we had always been interested in him because he owned some traction-engines and steam-rollers, which worked for the Kent County Council, and our friend 'the stout young man' who gave us a photograph of himself and his engine was employed by him. Mr. Arnold also owned a motor car, which was the first we had ever seen.

More than once we had watched him charging along in it—a red-bearded man talking in a loud voice to his passenger, and evidently regarding our hill as a final test of his panting 'two-and-a-half-horse Benz'. My brothers, who were mechanically minded and had been reading a book called *Carriages Without Horses Shall Go!* considered Mr. Arnold a gallant pioneer. But my mother and I were still inclined to treat motor cars as an eccentricity. Anyhow I felt that something unexpectedly nice was happening when she and I started off in the pony-cart, escorted by my brothers on their bicycles. It was a cloudless day in the middle of July—just the sort of day when one ought to stop learning arithmetic and go off into the blue distance where Mr. Arnold's launch was getting up steam. As we trotted over the railway bridge at Paddock Wood station I asked her how long it had been there, for I was looking at everything as though I had never seen it before, owing to the fact that we were going out on an adventure. The railway had been there about fifty years, she said; before that there had hardly been any houses there at all, which was why most of them had slate roofs and were so different from the pretty old thatched cottages and the one, about half-way to Mr. Arnold's mills, which used to have a toll-gate and had a house-leek on the roof and a thrush in a wicker cage hanging by the door. Mr. Arnold's house by the river was quite plain and very ugly; he had no time for being picturesque and had only built it to be a corn merchant in.

But his motor car was there and my mother was persuaded to get into it. How well I remember the moment when it began to move and she was carried slowly away, sitting stiffly upright, as though she expected the whole thing to blow up before it reached the main road.

'I regard it with the deepest suspicion,' she remarked facetiously when she alighted after a journey of about five hundred yards. Defensively polite, Mr. Arnold informed her that he'd been to Rochester and back last week, fifteen miles each way, without a shadow of a breakdown.

Soon afterwards we were on board the boat and ploughing peacefully toward Maidstone, with a couple of locks to go through, which made it even more interesting. Passing Wateringbury, we waved to Ted Avery, who was leaning on his boat-hook to watch us. We waved temperately, for we were feeling a little shy, though perfectly contented.

Mr. Arnold spent most of his time supervising the engine, emerging occasionally to say something about it in his loud voice to his friend at the tiller, who had been introduced to us as what sounded like 'Mr. Lelong'.

Mr. Lelong was wearing a very gaudy striped blazer, and had an impressive moustache and a strong-smelling cigar. He was most attentive to my mother, who conversed with him about the landscape in what we used to describe as 'her calling voice', which meant politeness tinged with reserve. 'Allow me to offer you another 'am sandwich. The open air makes one peckish, don't it?' said Mr. Lelong. Thus pressed to partake, my mother ate another. Though why I should mention a remembered ham sandwich after all these years I really don't know, unless it is because we had such a happy day on the Medway.

V

Ever since I could remember, I had been remotely aware of a lot of rich Sassoon relations. I had great-uncles galore, whom I had never met, and they all knew the Prince of Wales, who sometimes stayed with them at Brighton. One of them had been made into a baronet. Never having received so much as a chuck under the chin from any of these great-uncles, I couldn't exactly feel proud of them for being so affluent and having entertained the Shah of Persia when he was in England; but I was, as a matter of course, impressed by the relationship, and often wondered what they looked like.

The only Sassoon relation who meant anything to me so far was my father's sister, Auntie Rachel, whose proper name was Mrs. Frederick Beer. Her house was called 'Seven Chesterfield Gardens, Mayfair'. I was told that Mr. Beer had twenty thousand a year and that the marble staircase at

'Seven Chesterfield Gardens' had cost £20,000.

It never seemed a happy house, though, with its subdued atmosphere of wealth and well-trained servants. Twenty thousand a year couldn't create much merriment on those chilly marble stairs, or in the warm unventilated rooms with their lacquered Oriental furniture and the supposedly priceless pictures, which seemed less alive, somehow, than they ought to have been considering the prices that had been paid for them.

Auntie Rachel herself fitted in with her surroundings. Dark-haired, pale, and handsome, she always gave an impression of having slept badly the night before. It was as though the house had a devitalizing effect on her.

Such was the rather oppressive grandeur that awaited us when we scrambled out of the luxurious brougham which had brought us from Charing Cross station, where we had been met on the platform by the plump protective footman in his long brown livery coat and cockaded hat. The coachman, who might have been the footman's twin brother, smiled benevolently at us as we got in, and the sleek brown horses looked as though they'd never known an hour's anxiety about their next meal. At such a moment of arrival, as I am now visualizing it, London itself was rather like 'Seven Chesterfield Gardens', sombre and artificially lighted in the brown gloom of a winter's day; but we were as cosy as could be, wrapped in a furry rug, and clip-clopping along to Mayfair, while my mother reminded us that we really mustn't ask Auntie Rachel what she was going to buy for us when we went shopping with her after lunch on our way to Maskelyne and Cooke's mystery entertainment at the Egyptian Hall, where my elder brother had once been up on to the stage and had been unable to find out how the vanishing trick was done. Then the carriage drew up; the massive portico received us; the doors with their grille of gilded metal-work swung back, and we were safe inside, being bowed to by the solemn but delighted butler in the lofty marble hall, and deferentially disentangled from our overcoats by the brown-liveried footmen with their striped waistcoats and gilt buttons embossed with the Beer crest, which was a pelican feeding its young. (The crest was on almost everything—it was even clipped out on the back of the little black poodle Zulu.)

The downstairs drawing-room where we waited for Auntie Rachel was crowded with dim gilt Chinese cabinets which made one curious to know what was in them but were otherwise as dispiriting as the foggy antique mirrors, the glum-looking damasks and brocades, and the lilies and orchids which had obviously never lived out of doors.

Even Zulu, to whom we talked in subdued voices, was a rather pensive poodle and regarded us with listless eyes.

Auntie Rachel was well known for always being late for everything. She was vague and desultory, conversing with a hurried murmurous intensity which was rather difficult to catch. Her gaiety seemed absent-minded and when she smiled it was like an afterthought. Meanwhile the ornate French clock told another quarter in tired musical tones, and at last Auntie Rachel came rustling in, wearing a huge feathery hat, reticently affectionate, and smelling of violets as she offered a cold ivory cheek to each of us in turn.

Then the gong boomed obsequiously (so differently from the 'it's your own fault if you're late' bombilations of the oft-belaboured gong at home) and a move was made for the dining-room, which was approached by a corridor walled with glass and made like a bridge. On the bamboo bridge we always stopped to marvel at our multiplied and diminishing reflections, which couldn't be counted. There was electric light, too, which for us was something quite out of the ordinary. 'I can see simply hundreds of myself!' my younger brother would exclaim. And I would outdo him with 'I can see thousands and millions and trillions of myselves, getting tinier and tinier all the time, like ancestors!' Auntie Rachel, who always became less and less languid while we were with her, would laugh in her low-voiced expressive way, as though she were remembering half-forgotten happiness.

There was electric light in the dining-room also, as it had no windows. The food was a series of succulent surprises, and there were wonderful pictures on the walls. But every time we went there the floor became more densely occupied by piles of books. They were stacked all round the room and none of them had ever been opened, though they ought to have been because they were, to be precise, review copies sent to the *Sunday Times*, of which Auntie Rachel was the editor. (At that time both the *Observer* and the *Sunday Times*, which in those days were rather unobtrusive and retiring newspapers, belonged to Mr. Beer, whose father had been a financier.) Auntie Rachel used to send us a lot of the fairy books and children's stories which had hoped to be reviewed, but this made no difference to the mass of literature which encumbered the dining-room floor.

These books were only the overflow from the library, and by the time when she gave up being editor, which must have been about 1898, review copies were beginning to accumulate in the big drawing-room upstairs.

All Auntie Rachel's unshadowed years had been

before I could remember. She had married in 1887, when both she and Uncle Beer, as we called him, were well under thirty. According to my mother's account of him he was a most sweet-natured and charitable man, but after the first few years the doom of ill health descended on him, and even my earliest impression was of someone rather limp and aimless who drifted into the room with a cigar which seemed more an appurtenance than a cause of contentment to his gentle brown-bearded face. They had no children, and from the first I was aware of Auntie Rachel as a lonely rich woman with an ailing husband.

'Mr. Beer has no relations,' my mother used to tell us, without explaining the mystery of his deficient family tree. 'I am afraid poor Mr. Beer has a bad heredity,' she would say, thus adding to our mystification, for none of us had any notion what a heredity was. Apparently it was something to do with his mother having been an opera-singer, but that didn't seem a reason for his not being well enough to go for rides in Rotten Row on his park hack.

Auntie Rachel, however, refused to admit that he was becoming an invalid. Once, in 1897, when she was buying me a bat at Wisden's shop, she ordered a complete cricket outfit for Mr. Beer, practice net, stumps and all. 'The footmen can bowl to him down at Richmond,' she remarked casually. They had a house at Richmond which they had ceased to use, for by that time poor Mr. Beer was permanently upstairs, becoming paralysed and speechless, and we no longer saw him at all. Even then I was haunted by the pathetic futility of those cricket things which she had purchased for him.

She must have loved him very much, for she never gave up hoping that he would get well again, showing a brave, proud face to the world while she watched faithfully over him throughout his terrible lingering illness.

I have often wondered how the *Sunday Times* managed to appear once a week under her editorship. I have also wondered how the printers succeeded in deciphering her handwriting, which was the most illegible hieroglyphic I have ever puzzled over. When she wrote to us we used to have a family council to make out what her letter meant, and my mother used to shake her head and say that she was afraid poor Rachel was taking too many of those wretched sleeping draughts which Mr. Beer had got into the habit of, when his health began to fail.

In the winter of 1896 there was an event called 'The Press Bazaar at the Hotel Cecil'. Auntie Rachel had a stall, and my brothers and I were there as pages. Pages of the *Observer*, for we wore tabards with 'Observer' on them in ribboned letters. After the preliminary fuss of getting dressed up in one of the hotel bedrooms, we were stationed by the stall and told that when the Princess of Wales arrived we must sweep our plumed hats off like one page. In spite of rehearsals, the final effect was a failure. After waiting a long time, I became aware that something was about to happen; the crowd parted and I heard as in a dream someone talking in a very loud voice. An old gentleman with a red face and large white whiskers was coming toward me; he was speaking to a beautiful lady with dark hair done up like a crisp chrysanthemum, who moved in a slow and stately manner. My elder brother nudged me with his elbow, but I continued to stare at the funny old gentleman until my hat was knocked off by one of my brothers, who had swept theirs off in accordance with our instructions. Amused by my gaping embarrassment, the Princess of Wales, for she it was, smiled down at me and graciously remarked—'Never mind, little boy,' while Auntie Rachel curtsied, though not deeply enough to cover up my confusion. Such was my introduction to the Royal Family which my great-uncles had so often entertained at their houses. Grandmama Thornycroft had made marble portraits of all Queen Vic-

toria's children when they were infants, and all I
could do when the Princess and the Duke of
Cambridge came along was to get my hat knocked
off and stand there staring like a dolt! Auntie
Rachel consoled me afterwards by giving me a
copy of a little book called *The Time Machine*
signed by the author, but I didn't feel that I
deserved it.

★   ★   ★

Auntie Rachel seldom came to see us in the
country. When she did, it was, I think, usually
done on an impulse, when she felt in need of advice
from my mother, on whose judgment she relied, in
her vague way. I remember how she once missed
her train and took a 'special' one, from which she
emerged to creep up to our house in the village fly.

She looked out of place in the country. Away
from her own surroundings she seemed sallow and
untidy and almost eccentric, as if her elegant London clothes had been put on in a hurry. More
absent-minded than ever, too, though her amus-
ingness and charm were always apparent. While
we were showing her round the garden I picked
a rose for her, and couldn't help noticing when she
took it that her hand with its magnificent rings was
positively grimy. When had she last taken off her
rings, I wondered.

Afterwards she had a long murmuring conversation with my mother in the drawing-room, and then went back to London, as she always did, because she couldn't leave Uncle Beer for more than a few hours, and also had a lot of engagements, though goodness knows what they were.

Seeing her off in the fly, I probably thought what a pity it was that she couldn't stay in the country. I was too young to feel considerately sorry for her, as I should now, but there was a sense of sadness that she had gone back to her joylessly opulent Mayfair mansion where even the clocks seemed to have nothing to do, while I played cricket with my brothers—until we were called indoors from the dew-smelling garden and the evening sky reflected in the studio windows and the friendly old roller standing there with its handle up, where we'd left it to 'press down' a bumpy spot on our cricket pitch.

Auntie Rachel's failure to be happy bewildered me a bit, for I was just old enough to feel uneasy about life in an ignorant way. Already I associated poetry and music with an undefined heart-ache which I couldn't translate into my experience of sorrow. Had I been questioned I should have said nothing; but I thought of it as what I should have called 'a sort of *As You Like It* feeling'. Auntie Rachel had taken us to see the play a few months

before. It was the only time I'd been to a real
theatre, so far, and I almost wished I hadn't known
the names of the actors, for I wanted it to be a
lovely dream which belonged only to me. I wished
Auntie Rachel could be in a world like that—away
in the Forest of Arden, where there was nothing to
worry about and they sang 'Under the Green-
wood Tree' and gave me that heart-ache feeling
about happiness. I wanted her to be there and forget all about Mr. Beer's illness, and then go safely
back to a palace, where he would be waiting for
her, just as he was when she first knew him. And
I wanted to be there myself, helping Auntie Rachel
to enjoy herself. Mixed up with this was the idea
of Orpheus and Eurydice. In the hall at Auntie
Rachel's house there was a picture of them by
G. F. Watts. My mother had told me the story,
and it had been intensified when we went to an
afternoon party given by Auntie Rachel at which
an Act of Gluck's *Orpheus* had been performed.
The part of Orpheus was done by a celebrated
Italian singer, Julia Rivoli, who was a friend of
Auntie Rachel's. (Julia Neilson, by the way, had
been Rosalind in *As You Like It*.)

As I see it now, there was a comparison in my
mind between these two Julias—one winning perfect felicity, the other nobly tragic and frustrated.
I had a conflicting awareness of what I desired for

Auntie Rachel and of her doomed endeavour to bring back from the underworld of death that happiness which she had once known and which she refused to give up as lost beyond recovery.

VI

By the summer of 1897 it had become obvious that my brothers preferred their workshop to anything else. They were very important about it, and only played cricket with me and Mr. Moon when they could spare the time. My younger brother had lost interest in moths and butterflies, so I did most of my collecting alone. Even 'The Build' had been left to tumble down, though there was some talk of building a really up-to-date one in another part of the garden.

Their workshop was in the old cottage beyond the studio. The ground floor was still used for keeping garden tools and faggots in, and the mowing-machines also lived there; but the onions had been ousted from the upstairs room (though the smell remained) and a lathe and a carpenter's bench had been brought in. I can't remember what they did with the lathe, but they were very busy. They soldered things together, made bits of iron red-hot and then hit them with a hammer, and took in a paper called *The English Mechanic* which supplied them with fresh ideas. They also took out the works of the Queen Elizabeth clock in the dining-room and gave them a good oiling. The clock was never the same again; in fact it gave up going. Making things or else finding out how they had been made—that was what my brothers liked now; and while they were at work they were always singing a comic song which I was sick of hearing: 'Our lodger's such a nice young man, such a nice young man is he, *so* good, *so* kind, to all the family. . . .' The only bit of fun I got was when they broke several of the bulbous gun-metal handles off the studio windows, bored and 'turned' them into shiny brass cannons, melted a clock-weight into bullets, and fired them at the vinery from the workshop window. How far the bullets went no one ever discovered; we heard no sound of shattered glass, however, though we used real gunpowder—purloined from the potting-shed, where Reeves kept his old blunderbuss for shooting at jays and bullfinches.

But I knew how to enjoy being by myself. I could always take my fishing tackle down to the pond in the far corner of the steep orchard below the stable, which was several hundred yards away from the house. There I could feel contentedly cut off from the rest of the world, for Tom Richardson never came down to the pond and wouldn't have interfered with me if he had. All through a sleepy summer afternoon, the clink of his pail up in the stable-yard and the grunting sound of the chaff-cutter in the barn were the only noises which reminded me that he was there; and on Saturdays he was sure to be away playing in a cricket match.

The orchard pond contained some fair-sized roach and gudgeon; carp and tench were supposed to be there also, but were so far unverified by capture. And although it was small I could make it seem larger by thinking of it as a lake in some foreign land. Like most things, the pond had a past history of its own. (Richardson said it needed cleaning out, and at one end it certainly was getting shallow, owing to mud silting in with the runnel which came down the ditch under the hedge.) I didn't want to know too much about its matter-of-fact antecedents; but there was no denying that when old Harrison Weir had first stocked it with fish it must have been quite a well-kept pond. Anyhow that had been long before I was born. Now that it was in its meridian of deterioration and neglect, I wanted it to remain the same—with the fish leading their idle loitering lives and getting larger and more mysterious, and me only wanting to catch them so as to see what they looked like out of the water; for I knew that they didn't taste at all nice when cooked. I had been told that Harrison Weir used to keep his prize fowls in the orchard; Buff Orpingtons and Cochin-Chinas were the names which occurred to me; he also used to do drawings of them, for he was quite a well-known nature artist. The workshop had been his studio, and I thought of him as a rather fussy little man with a scrubby sort of beard and a reddish nose, though I had never seen him. I vaguely associated him with things I liked, but I didn't much care for his animal drawings, some of which were in one of my Natural History books. The only thing I really had against him was the way he had added on to our house, which my mother always said was 'full of waste space and designed without decorum'. Its chief absurdity was a tiled spire, which towered to a height of sixty feet from the road on which the house stood and also made the chimneys smoke. Harrison Weir used to have a large lamp lit in the tower every night, so that people down in the valley could see it and say 'That's where Harrison Weir lives'— to which the obvious reply was 'Is it weally!'— the name of our house being Weirleigh.

Anyhow in Harrison Weir's time the old cottage, now muffled in ivy to the top of its single chimney, had been his unpretentious studio. (It was as difficult to imagine it not smelling of onions as it was to imagine my mother's much grander one without its pleasantly familiar redolence of turpentine.)

Sitting under the apple tree by the pond I wondered why I was so unpractical, compared with my brothers. . . . I couldn't even draw decently with my coloured chalk pencils—or my coloured inks either, I thought, as I gazed indolently at a huge white crinkly cloud which seemed like time standing still, so quiet was the afternoon. And when I copied out my poems for my mother they always went untidy after the first few words and never began at the right place on the page. Auntie Rachel had given me a toy printing-press, but I had made a hopeless muddle of trying to print Gray's *Elegy* (two lines at a time). Apart from the ink smudges, I couldn't get the d's and b's quite right, and the second stanza had read something like this:

'Now fabes the glimmering landscape on the sight,
  And all the air a solemn stillness holds,
  Save where the beetle wheels his broning flight,
  And browsy tinklings lull the bistant folds.'

'Browsy tinklings' at any rate was almost like an improvement on the original version, I pondered, leaning my back against the trunk of the old apple tree, with only half my attention on my blue and red float, while skimming dragon-flies bemused me with their timeless flittings to and fro. Motionless as a shadow, I waited for a bite; but the float refused to bob, and the hum of insects was like an eternal siesta. Sunbeams, filtering past the pond-reflected branches, explored the oblivion of that underworld with their drowned translucency; very slowly, across the daydream water glades between the weeds and rotting snags, cruised the oldest of those uncatchable carp, in tantalizing aloofness, making the orchard and the woodland below it seem tranced and strange with expectancy. Alone with my tin of bait and my wool-gatherings, I was in an undisturbed world of my own, localized and satisfying as such worlds always are.

When I'd had enough of fishing I would become busy, improving the shores of the pond. At the end where the water trickled away under the hedge, someone had once made a dam with stakes and pieces of plank; enough remained to prevent the water running away too much. I called this the lagoon, and it had a thriving water-side population of water-boatmen and water-beetles. Minnows, alas, were absentees, but frogs were to be found there. The pond also contained rich deposits of white clay with which I made a snug little port, with jetties and roadsteads and the lighthouse and coastguard station a bit farther round the bay. In squelching self-absorption I talked to myself as I thought it all out, adding one improvement after another and ignoring the irresponsible behaviour of the water-boatmen and other inhabitants. Tadpoles were a problem. As long as they were tadpoles it was impossible to pretend that they were anything different, and I was thankful when they became nice little frogs who hopped away to seek their fortunes in the wild-flower forest. Water-snails, on the other hand, seemed to have much more reliable personalities than tadpoles.

Leaving my fishing tackle and a few small fish under the apple tree to be called for on my way home, I climbed over the hedge and was in Gedges Wood, which quite easily became something else. In the sun-flecked shade under the leafy chestnut poles there was a smell of wild garlic; and there were cushions of moss between the roots of oak trees where I could sit and listen; or I could clamber into the upper branches and be a look-out man in the full glory of the happy late afternoon sunshine. Or I would go on until I arrived at the banks of a small stream which lost itself in some marshy ground at the foot of the hill. This was a rushy region where there was a moorhen's nest among the sedges, and there was a jungle path through it where the thistles and ragwort grew higher than my head. It was a famous place for moths and butterflies. There were Cinnabar moths and lazy marsh-ringlets and three kinds of skippers (Dingy, Chequered, and Grizzled). I once told my mother that I'd seen a Purple Emperor there, and her sympathetic enthusiasm almost made me believe that I had; and anyhow it was the sort of place where I ought to have seen one.

Gedges Wood belonged to one of May and Bessie's brothers, and the long carriage road to his house on the hill-top went past the kingcup country where the moorhen lived. When I heard the rumble of his four-wheeled dogcart I tried to forget who he was, and enjoyed the adventure of his not knowing that I was there as I reconnoitred him from the edge of the undergrowth. (It was all the better because he usually pretended to be rather fierce when he did happen to find one in the wood.) There he was, anyhow, jogging along from Paddock Wood station, on his way home from London, where he'd been looking after the paper-mill that he was a partner in. Flies buzzed round his horse's ears; the groom-gardener was on the back seat, and he'd got that pink evening paper, *The Globe*, on his knee. The stop-press scores of to-day's county cricket were in it; these I should have liked to take a squint at. But I'd just been on the banks of the Zambesi River, where anything might happen if you waited long enough; my boots were full of rusty marsh water and I'd seen some very interesting newts. By the time the dog-cart had rumbled out of hearing I was an unflusterable character in one of H. Rider Haggard's stories, drying my feet in the sun and wishing I could make a fire and cook the evening meal. Up at the house the pump-yard bell might ring a second time for tea, but what did I care, even if the other two had eaten up all the cucumber sandwiches and every one was wondering why I was so late?

VII

Over the mantelpiece in the best spare bedroom there was a long frame with about ten photographs in it. A few of the people in the frame were relations; the others I had either seen or had heard about from my mother until I felt as if I knew them. Auntie Rachel was there, in fancy dress, looking young and lovely, standing against a screen with one arm lifted, holding a long-handled Burmese fan. Next to her was poor Mr. Beer, who had only a moustache and small whiskers then; he was wearing a tweed tail-coat and a brown billycock, and had a stick in his hand and one foot on a rustic seat.

After him came Mr. Belcher, the architect who had designed the studio and the stables (and would have added on to the house if it hadn't, most unluckily, been added on to already by Harrison Weir). Mr. Belcher had a neatly cut beard and pince-nez which looked like falling off. He'd been to stay with us once and hadn't seemed at all famous, but that may have been because he was so kind and was my elder brother's godfather. Sir Benjamin Baker came next. He had built the Forth Bridge and was a very great friend of my mother and her family. I'd never seen him, but he had a dark drooping moustache, and was rather like one of the generals in our book on the Indian Mutiny.

Laura Tadema and Nellie Gosse were sisters, but were in separate photographs. My mother seemed to be equally fond of them both. Laura Tadema was the wife of Alma Tadema the celebrated painter, who had sent us that red wine all the way from Italy last winter in fibre-plaited flasks. It had been a great excitement, unpacking them and thinking that even the straw had come from Italy. 'Dear Tadema is so much more festive than his pictures,' my mother had remarked, as she arranged the wine-bottles on a shelf in the store-room. 'He makes the marble the most important part of the picture,' she had added.

Nellie Gosse was married to Mr. Gosse, who was the only author who had ever given me one of his books. I felt that he must be a very nice man because he had put Mr. before my name in his inscription, though it was only my tenth birthday when he sent the book, which was called *Th*

Naturalist of the Sea Shore and was the life of his father. I had only read the last two pages so far (more than nine months afterwards), but at the end, where his father died, there was a quotation which I liked so much that I had put it into one of my poems, wondering who it was by and whether my mother would notice the difference. The lines were:

'Now came still evening on, and twilight grey
  Had in her sober livery all things clad.'

The photograph of Mrs. Gosse was taken from a portrait of her by Theodore Blake Wirgman. Next to it was a photograph of his sister Miss Wirgman. I didn't know Theodore, but I knew Helen Wirgman very well, and never thought of her as anything except 'Wirgie'.

In the photograph, however, she looked unlike her real self. She was wearing a low-necked evening dress, with a piece of black velvet tied round her throat in a bow, and had a rather grand ornament in her hair, which hadn't begun to go grey then. She had been taken side-face too, with a sort of smoothed-out expression, which wasn't how I thought of her, though the photograph showed how handsome she was.

Wirgie was a bit more rugged-looking, really—specially when she was listening to someone who

made her feel unfriendly, which happened now
and again. Anyhow she was devoted to Uncle
Don, who was next to her in the frame, standing
on the bridge of his steam yacht *Thetis* dressed
like a ship's captain. Wirgie often stayed with the
Donaldsons, and my cousins (five boys and five
girls) adored her. She had rebuked me once and
made me feel very small because I made a joke
about Uncle Don being so stout.

'Your Uncle Don is one of the kindest and
most humorous men in the world,' she had said
and had been quite huffy with me for several hours
afterwards, though she knew that I loved Uncle Don
very much and had sent him some of my poems.
He was a great engineer too, and had come home
from India (where he was embanking the River
Hooghly) to help Uncle John start the Thorny
croft works, which had been set going as much by
his ability as by Uncle John's inventive genius.

All the photographs were of my mother's friends
as they used to be before she 'began to see so little
of them'. There was a sort of 'happy past' feeling
about them—the same as the room had felt like
when I was lying there getting well after pneumonia and my mother was telling me about them
as they were when she first knew them, in the old
days when she had been an Academy student and
Laura and Nellie used to go with her to the 'Mon-

day Pops' at St. James's Hall to hear Joachim and Madame Schumann.

I couldn't remember a time when the photographs hadn't been there. I didn't try to think out the feeling that they gave me, but they all seemed as if they never expected to look different from what they were, all those years ago. When I was alone in the spare room I used to think how queer it was that I should be looking at them like that without their knowing who I was or that there would ever be such a person as me at all. It was confusing but vaguely enjoyable, especially now, when a blackbird was singing in the arbutuses below the open window. There they all were, being photographed—Sir Benjamin Baker before he built the Forth Bridge, and Mr. Belcher before he built our studio, and Mr. Beer before he lost his health—and none of them had the ghost of an idea that they would some day belong to our best bedroom just as much as the jugs and basins on the washstand with the funny-faced blue fishes swimming about on them. The only one who really did know was Wirgie, for she had stayed with us last summer. And now, a year later, she was coming again, that very afternoon. My mother, who was busy putting flowers in water, had asked me to carry some sweet-williams and mignonette up to the spare room, and I was thinking how well the name Wirgie suited her, for it reminded me of her low, mouth-closed laugh, and her slow way of speaking. Sniffing the mignonette as I put it on the mantelpiece, I knew that she would be just the same as ever, though last summer was such a long time ago. It seemed only yesterday that we'd caught that Red Underwing down by the rhubarb. This evening I would show her how much I'd improved my collection since then. And how pleased she would be to see the cats, and my tortoise Joey in whose habits and character she had taken such a friendly interest.

*　　　*　　　*

When I was ten or eleven years old I could see that most people were unlike one another; you could tell that even from those photographs in the spare room. But Wirgie was different from other people in a different way. For one thing, she sometimes got into bad tempers without quite knowing why, as I did myself, and this made me feel that we understood one another. I could never be sure what she was going to get upset about; it came on like a thunderstorm and was soon over, though rather disquieting while it lasted. When Wirgie got into a wax and glowered, the thing to do was to leave her alone for a bit and when I saw her again she would be nicer than ever and make me forget how we'd walked all the way home from Water-cress Well without saying a word just because I'd prodded a toad rather hard so as to see how fast it could go when it was in a hurry. Anyhow it taught me how fond she was of toads.

I had long since learnt that what she disliked most was spiders. Myself, I found them interesting, but it was hardly safe for me even to think of one when Wirgie was about. Many a time I had piloted her past spiders which looked as if they were under a magnifying glass, magnified as they were by my anxiety lest she should observe them.

There was no doubt, however, that the most important thing about Wirgie was her piano playing. It seemed suitable, too, that she played Beethoven sonatas so splendidly—better even than Paderewski, I thought, though I'd only heard him once, at Tunbridge Wells, and that had been when I was too young to listen to him properly. When she was playing the last movement of the Moonlight Sonata, or the first page of the Pathétique, I felt that she was expressing all the stormy and tremendous things which she couldn't say in any other way, and I wanted to be able to feel like that myself. She was nowhere near being a professional, but behind her playing there was, as I afterwards realized, the power of an intense imagination and an emotional warmth and vitality which cannot be learnt from professors. It was wonderfully exciting to listen to her, but of course one didn't want it to go on all the evening, and she always closed the piano just when I was thinking how nice it would be to have a good game of dumb crambo before it was time to go to bed. And, when she and I had gone out of the room, and the others had 'thought of a word that rhymed with shawl', she would crawl and sprawl and bawl as if dumb crambo were the only thing in the world worth doing. (She could act tragic parts too, and my mother said she ought to have been on the stage.) What I liked about Wirgie was that she could behave as if she were quite young and yet make me feel that I was almost as grown up as she was. She knew all about nonsense too, and when I was excited and lost control of my thoughts and said anything that came into my head, such as, 'The studio was playing Ludo with a poodle in a puddle', she never told me not to be silly, but merely remarked that she'd always thought such things only happened in the game called Consequences when you unfolded the paper and read the result.

She didn't mind exploring prickly places either, and would go anywhere when she had a butterflynet in her hand. She realized that if one missed catching a Black-Veined White one would never see another as long as one lived, though it always turned out to be a Green-Veined White when caught. I can remember her trampling wildly across the wire-netting which had been stretched over the garden pond in case we fell in; we had been on it so often that it had sagged considerably and one's feet were in the water all the time; but Wirgie went up and down the middle like an acrobat on the safety-net at a circus. And she was always ready to go out and beat the bushes for moths, though it was a joke of ours that practically the only ones that flew out of the lilacs and laurus-tinuses were Pimpernel Pugs. (The Pimpernel Pug is a small dingy yellow moth which would be uninteresting even if it were extremely rare.)

Wirgie was more than forty years older than I was. I never asked her anything about her early life, but it did seem strange to think of her having lived all that time without my knowing what she was doing. She had been there all through those old bound volumes of *Punch* and had read *Alice in Wonderland* when it first came out, and here she was, sitting in the schoolroom after tea, mending a hole in my butterfly-net while I put a pin through a Pepper-and-Salt Moth. It was difficult to imagine her as grown up when ladies still wore crinolines, and still more difficult to imagine her wearing one. Probably she had refused to, I thought, remembering how she had bounced up and down on the wire-netting with her feet under water. She hadn't much money to live on, but she had been abroad a lot and spoke both French and German. Mr. Moon made learning geography dull; but when Wirgie told me about foreign places they became real and interesting. Mr. Moon had never been anywhere; he could only point out places on a shiny coloured map which unrolled with a rumpling sound when he hung it on the blackboard. That was only teaching. I could never remember how high Mont Blanc was; but when Wirgie pointed to a white cloud behind some rainy ones on the horizon, and said that the Alps were like that, I felt I knew, and ceased to associate Mont Blanc with blancmange.

Anyhow I can see her sitting there in the schoolroom, telling me about Europe and making me imagine some of it quite clearly against the background of its mysterious immensity—until my brothers came cluttering along the passage and the spell was broken by their return from the workshop. That word *mysterious* always reminds me of Wirgie; I can hear her intonation of it as though she were with me now; and I remember how she used to quote one of her favourite lines— 'darker grows the valley, more and more forgetting'—when we were looking across the Weald while dusk was falling and away in the hayfields beyond the wood a nightjar churred endlessly on as though it could make June stay with us for ever.

On such an evening we would go out after dinner to look at the tree trunks which we had smeared with rum and treacle. Neither of us knew precisely what moths were in season at midsummer, but my bull's-eye lantern, which smelt of scorching paint, glowed with our expectancy that on some tree trunk we should find a Ghost Moth or a Tiger Moth or even a Death's Head Hawk Moth. We never did; but the syringa bushes were in bloom, and we could hear a nightingale far down the wood, and the scattered lights along the darkness of the valley were like homely stars.

*   *   *

On the morning of the twenty-second of June I stood on the lawn and gazed through the glassy heat at the far-off hills, saying to Wirgie— 'Won't it be exciting when we see all the bonfires burning to-night?' She was wearing her garden-party dress; she called it 'my old, old mulberry silk garment', but it suited her and she looked very distinguished in it. I was feeling elated, for it was Diamond Jubilee Day. Mr. Moon had, of course, granted us a whole holiday, and we were just off to see Bessie planting the Jubilee Oak on the village green.

From a long way off I can hear the click of Wirgie's pink parasol as she puts it up. That little click, preceded by a faint creak of stretching silk, seems to fix these retrospections at a point from which I can behold the Kentish Weald as though it were the future which awaited me. (And while I do so Wirgie catches my eye, through her white veil, with that deeply humorous glance of hers which understood me so thoroughly.)

Looked at from our lawn, the Weald was, in my opinion, as good a view as anyone could wish to live with. You could run your eyes along more than twenty miles of a low-hilled horizon never more than ten or twelve miles away. The farthest distance had the advantage of being near enough for its details to be, as it were, within recognizable reach. There was, for instance, a small party of pine trees on the skyline toward Maidstone which seemed to be keeping watch on the world beyond —a landmark on the limit of my experience they always seemed, those sentinel pines. I often looked at them through my toy telescope. The idea of the places beyond those hills was a physical sensation which I experienced with ignorant relish while I gazed 'into the blue distance'. That Rochester, Chatham, and Strood could possibly be unattractive towns was a thought which had never occurred to me. The foreground was an easy-going prospect of meadows, orchards, and hop-gardens, supervised by the companionable cowls of hop-kilns (or oast-houses, if you prefer it). The Medway was there, winding lazily past Wateringbury on its way to Sheerness, where Uncle Don went when the destroyers from the Works were being tried; he always called the Medway the Mudway, and thought the Thames a much better river. Sometimes, in quiet weather, I could just hear from beyond the horizon, a faint muffled thud, which meant, I was told, that they were testing a big naval gun at Sheerness.

Leisurely trains went along the valley, up to London and down to the coast, whistling derisively when they bustled through our station without stopping; goods trains loitered along with clanking buffers, whistling in a good-humoured way, and reduced by distance to the size of a toy apparatus.

And there was I, for whom, at the age of eleven, London meant little more than going up for the day to see Auntie Rachel or 'the Dons' as we called Uncle Don and his family. For me the future didn't even provide the prospect of going to school, for my mother was opposed to the idea of our leaving home. To-morrow I should be rambling heedlessly in the wood or angling by the orchard pond, dreamily inheriting the scents and rumours of 1897, ignorant in that sunlight of long ago where a dallying bee buzzed humdrum happy summer for me while the statesmen of Europe provided material for Tenniel's weekly cartoon in *Punch*. Looking across the Weald I foresaw nothing but the Jubilee bonfires which were ready to be set alight that evening. Up in London dear old Queen Victoria was driving through the streets with a bevy of foreign princes tit-tupping along behind her carriage, and every one feeling as if she was their grandmother. No one could tell what was going to happen any more than I could see beyond our safe-looking hills. While Wirgie played the piano after dinner people were jingling out to the Opera in hansom-cabs. A brilliant season was in full swing around them, and they knew as little of their future insecurity as my tortoise Joey, who died the next winter of being dug up to see how he was getting on while hibernating.

VIII

If I could return to Weirleigh on some ordinary-looking morning in August 1897, I should find the place rather pauseful and absent-minded. Peter, our plebeian old tabby cat, would be crouching intently under an Irish yew near the pigeon's bath while the white fantails pecked up maize. Lizzy the housemaid would be shaking her duster out of an upstairs window. Mrs. Battersen the cook (my mother called all cooks Mrs. whether married or not, saying that it gave them status) would be making plum jam and singing to herself in the kitchen, the scullery maid having gone home for her holiday. There would be silence in the studio; the colossal plaster figure of the Fighting Gladiator would be alone with the odour of oil-paints while an imprisoned butterfly fluttered drily against the skylight. In the drawing-room, alone with its aroma of pot-pourri and the smell of newly bees-waxed parquet floor, the large etchings of Mason's *Harvest Moon* and Walker's *Harbour of Refuge* would be taking a rest from being taken for granted by eyes accustomed to them. In the dining-room, the Greek head, which I always thought of as Medusa (but really it was Hypnos) would be staring sightlessly at the crippled Queen Elizabeth clock from the top of the carved oak cupboard; but Hypnos, who had been painted green to look like old bronze, would lack the lumps of sugar which we were in the habit of putting into his eye-holes.

Even the view of the Weald from the dining-room windows would seem to know that our house was having a quiet time, and would have assumed a daydreaming look while cloud-shadows travelled along the August indolence of its green-muffled miles.

Nothing much would be happening at Weirleigh. We had all gone to the Norfolk coast for a change of air, and for the time being our address was Edingthorpe Rectory, which my mother had taken for two months—after making quite certain that there was nothing wrong with its drains. Everything at Weirleigh would be looking extremely ordinary—in August 1897—if by some chronological miracle my 1937 self could return there.

At the front gate I should pull the bell-handle

and hear it ring remotely below the back stairs.
Waiting outside the front door, I should wonder
whether *vero nihil verius*, which Harrison Weir
had caused to be carved above the entrance, was
dog Latin, and whether it meant 'nothing is truer
than truth'. Ringing the bell and asking to be
allowed to walk in and have a look at one's past!
All the world would like to do that, for the sense
of the past is strong in us—as strong as our awareness of the irremediable errors in it.

In mind-sight we return: but even if in more
than mind-sight we could somehow be there in the
actuality of outlived experience, we should be
strangers, invisible, and powerless to avert so
much as the overwinding of a clock.

'Don't do it; don't do it!' we should cry, dis-
cerning in some blindly enacted blunder the first
step taken on some very wrong road. But the
warning would be like dumb shoutings in a dream.
Not by one faintest whisper could we safeguard
our vanished self while he gaily or sullenly created
the sorrow and bitterness of after days. Those eyes
of youth would look past us even as they look past
the troubled faces of those who try to help them.

In the meantime, Lizzy the housemaid answers
the front door bell. 'They've gone to Norfolk,'
she says, wiping her hands on her apron. The
gentleman who stares at her, half smiling, as

though he remembered her, reminds her somehow
of Master Siegfried; perhaps he's a relation, she
thinks, and then looks again and sees that it's only
old Mr. Moon after all, and quite different from
what she thought she'd seen. Mr. Moon has called
to ask, in his humble punctilious way, whether he
can pick a few of the figs from the tree on the
pump-yard wall—Mrs. Sassoon having very kindly
given him permission to gather some fruit and
flowers during her absence. He too may catch a
telepathic glimpse of the sympathetic stranger from
1937, as he treads respectfully in with his basket
while Lizzy disappears down the steps toward the
servant's hall, where cook is flapping a wasp away
from the Golden Syrup tin on the table and the
grey parrot (who wasn't taken to Norfolk after all)
dubiously consumes an over-ripe plum. And then
an unexpected gust of wind slams the door on the
past.

*   *   *

To transfer myself to Edingthorpe should have
been scarcely the work of a moment. But when I
tried to do so, mind-sight was unable to recreate
the place. It had been a transient experience, and
for many years I had almost forgotten about it.

While we are growing up we discard the past
with heartless superiority. We have no time to stop

and think tenderly about it. Later on Edingthorpe gradually became a memory which haunted my mind, but I couldn't see it at all distinctly. There was only one way out of the difficulty; and that was to transfer myself back there in my motor car and find out what it really had been like.

So I drove to North Walsham, a small town which hadn't altered much since I last saw it, except that there were motors, and more people in the main street, though that may have been because it was market-day. I had forgotten that the church tower, which had fallen down about a hundred years before, so the sexton told me, had never been rebuilt and still looked as if it had behaved patriotically in a modern war. But there had been no battle at North Walsham since the Peasant's Revolt in 1381, and the final collapse of the tower had been caused by a great gale.

From North Walsham I made for Edingthorpe, in almost sultry sunshine, on an August afternoon. In the old days that five-mile drive had been quite an undertaking; but now, although I cruised with affectionate slowness, I couldn't make the journey take more than fifteen minutes. There it was, however—the same humdrum agricultural landscape, and the now well-remembered road along which we had jogged dustily in the Rectory carriage, seldom meeting anything except a lumbering farm

waggon or a tradesman's gig. It happened that I
met no one at all this time; going into the past
forty years afterwards, seemed almost as easy as
thinking oneself back there. I had only to sit, with
one finger on the steering-wheel, and stare around
me. Everything was very quiet, as though it were
keeping quite still so that I could have a good look
at it. Leaving the main road, about a mile from
the Rectory, I was relieved to find that the lane
was as narrow and unassuming as ever. The wild
convolvulus still twined exuberantly over the low
hedges, and the level landscape receded as prosily
as it had done in 1897, when it really was a long
way from anywhere, and looked like it—as indeed
it still did. Edingthorpe, thank goodness, was still
a straggling hamlet a few miles inland from the
east coast, and the almost unidentifiable post office
had merely been moved from one dear old cottage
to another.

The parish, I thought, appears to have changed
less than I have; and my fifty-year-old face agreed
with me from the bit of looking-glass on the wind-
screen. Beginning to look all its age now, that face
—though able to accept the fact with a confidential
smile, and exchange with its reflection a philoso-
phic and good-humoured grimace. For I had
lunched at a dozy unmodernized hotel in North
Walsham, contentedly alone in the shabby coffee-

room, and I was having a holiday from writing my reminiscences.

Slower and slower I drove, until I came to the signpost where four lanes meet. There was the black stagnant pond with a few ducks on it—longer and narrower than it had been in my rememberings, as well as being on the other side of the road from where mind-sight had placed it. It had always been an unprepossessing, unfishable pond. On the opposite bank were some trees which I couldn't remember; then I reminded myself that those rather dingy elms and alders had been mere saplings forty years ago.

The farm across the road had at any rate improved with time. Its thatched barns and grey stone house were unchanged, but my eyes had learned how to appreciate them.

And here was the mellow-faced little cottage where we used to buy our bull's-eyes and acid-drops from a scrutinizing old woman who sat there all day at her needlework. Nothing was for sale now, but the notice-board was still nailed over the door. *Hannah Pestell, licensed to sell tobacco*—the words could just be made out. Had she been here still I should have opened the bell-jangling door and bought something. But the cottage appeared to be locked up; there was nobody about at the farm either; and now I came to think of it,

I hadn't seen a soul since I left North Walsham.
Wool-gathering being an essentially solitary pas-
time, circumstances had so far been favourable.

Things will begin to come back to me soon, I
thought. Leaving the car at the crossroads, I
strolled up the lane. The Rectory was only a couple
of hundred yards away now, and I felt quite excited. My memory of the house had been like a
faded old photograph, obsolete and empty. But
when I leant my elbows on the front gate I saw a
fragment of 1897 quite clearly. There hadn't been
those prosperous fuchsias below the windows then,
but it was just such an afternoon as this and just
about the same time of day (three o'clock by my
watch). The house was very quiet now—left to
look after itself, apparently, like everything else at
Edingthorpe—but in 1897 we are just starting off
for the seashore. The odd-man gardener has
brought the Rectory shandrydan round to the
front door—it was a low elongated open vehicle
drawn by a mild old mare named Lucy. My
mother, in that old purple cloak of hers, is packing herself in with the picnic-basket and bathing
gear, and Tessa Gosse (dear Nellie's 'jolly decent'
elder daughter) is with her. My brother Michael
is on his bicycle, with one foot on the ground
while my younger brother Hamo and I are mount-
ing our donkeys. I have just remembered that I've

forgotten my sand-shoes, so I dash back into the house while my mother begs Hamo not to allow the donkeys to eat the laurels and poison themselves.

When the cavalcade has moved off, Emily Eyles is left on the doorstep exclaiming that the mistress has gone off without her sunshade after all. Old Frank, the odd-man, who is also the village wiseacre, remarks that she ought to be glad to feel the sun on her face and returns philosophically to his gardening, while Emily trips indoors to tidy things up and meditate about Mr. Dawson, her young man, who has saved up just enough to start a little shop of his own with, when they get married next year. Washing up the plates and dishes, Emily sings a sentimental ballad about sailing ships. 'White wings that never grow weary,' she warbles, her clear young voice guilelessly audible as I lean my elbows on the gate. And then, as I lift my elbows from the gate and listen again, the only sound I hear is the whir of a reaping-machine in the glebe field below the churchyard. The cavalcade has departed, not through the gate, which is shut, but through my mind, which is open to the past and its harmonious vibrations. And what I was enjoying most, since I had nothing very wonderful to remember, was the feeling of being actually there, in that place which I had thought of so

often since I last saw it. I had been wise to keep
this experience in reserve until I was ripe to make
the most of it. Later on I would explore the garden
for memories; in the meantime I struck across a
stubble-field toward the church, which could be
seen on a knoll about half a mile away.

The church caught me napping. I had failed to
remember that it had a thatched roof. Surely I
must have been aware of that in 1897. But I could
only remember an hour-glass in an iron frame on
the pulpit, and how the earnest-featured young
locum tenens parson had once interrupted his sermon by striding swiftly down to eject some mis-
behaving village boy. I would have liked to know
that the hour-glass was still there—to turn it over
and watch the trickling sand; but the church door
was locked and I couldn't see much of the interior
through the narrow plain-glass windows. So I
walked slowly round the graveyard, which was just
sufficiently neglected to be pleasing, and observed
for the first time that the lantern tower was octa-
gonal. In old days I had felt a casual affection for
the church, and had liked the idea of it having been
built in the thirteenth century. But I realized now
that it had a very special dignity and simplicity,
standing there on its low hill above the harvest
fields as though it were the faithful servant of the
life around it.

It was indeed the church of a far-off childhood, with its single bell that called to us across the fields at sundown—for there was only an evening service while we were at Edingthorpe. All churches are alike in the eyes of our Maker, it now seemed to be saying; and it evoked in me a sense of local England and of the simple old centuries behind it —the harvests it had seen, and the pathos of those humble folk who had toiled and died and had been 'of this parish'.

Well remembered, too, it must have been, I thought, by the men who went far away and never returned. For I was standing before the lych-gate now—that new-comer which had been there less than twenty years. Its carved lettering told me that it was in loving memory of a young lance-corporal of the Norfolk Regiment.

'He fought at Mons, Le Câteau, The Marne, The Aisne, The First Battle of Ypres, and at Hill 60, and went down in the torpedoed Transport *Royal Edward* in the Aegean Sea, 13th August 1915.'

Reading the date of his death, I couldn't help feeling that it was a strange coincidence that to-day should also be August 13th. It was as if someone had prepared this little surprise for me so as to make my revisitation seem pre-arranged and alight with latent significance. Here anyhow was one who must have remembered that little church on the green rising ground, for his father had been rector for nineteen years and was buried close to the lych-gate.

The inscription, so carefully spaced along the beams, had no doubt been his. Not hastily had he chosen that epitaph in Latin:

'Qui procul hinc . . . Mediterraneis sepultus sub undis . . . Qui ante diem periit, sed miles, sed pro patria.'

'Sed miles, sed pro patria.' Those were words about which the world had since been trying to make up its mind, in its half-hearted renouncement of war, in its heavily armed pursuit of peace. Yet, in the shadow of that gate, in that moment of my mind, the words were beautiful and unbitter —they brought tears to my eyes as I looked away from them at the afternoon sunshine and the barley field and the horses going slowly along with the reaping-machine. Here, surely, was the gate to the past toward which I had made this pilgrimage. For it was in the autumn of 1915 that my brother Hamo had been buried at sea after being mortally wounded on the Gallipoli Peninsula—he whom I had idly remembered as a little boy on a donkey. 'Don't let the donkeys eat the laurels!' my mother had said to him. . . . Laurels and donkeys. The donkeys who made the Great War were generous enough with their laurels, I thought. Then I decided that I must give up feeling bad-tempered about it, or I should be ruining my afternoon. So I picked a poppy and a cornflower and put them on a ledge under the lych-gate, and then went placidly down to the farm lane, over the stile and along the path which led through a little meadow to the Rectory garden. As I went, I agreed with myself that I had been right about the unforgettable flavour of Edingthorpe. What was the explanation of its hold on my mind, I wondered. It seemed to be aware that it had never been anything but a thorpe and would remain one in perpetuity. This, perhaps, was its appealing quality—that it had no expectancy of being sought out again by anyone who had known it in years gone by. It was friendly, but quite content to be lost sight of and forgotten, not speaking until it was spoken to. Anyhow it had been meeting me more than half-way that afternoon, like some shy untalented person responding to sympathetic encouragement.

And here I was, close to the house again and entering the nut orchard which I used to be so fond of, and to which I had so often gone when I wanted to be alone. Shady and flecked with sunbeams, its tangled untidy grass was just the same;

but how small it looked and how unready to be revisited. I too was unready for the queer feeling it gave me. It looked so ordinary, and yet so far away from the present time. And how easily it showed me myself as I once was—a boy in a brown jersey and corduroy shorts bleached by many washings, sitting in the long grass with his knees up to his chin, reading *The Invisible Man*, which he had brought out there because one of his brothers had tried to tell him how it ended and he didn't want to be told. He doesn't look up or move as I stand beside him—that H. G. Wells-absorbed boy with reddish-brown hair. He knows nothing of himself, nothing of the delusions and discontents which he must muddle his way out of before he can be looked back on, almost as though he were someone in another life. Reading *The Invisible Man* in its blood-red binding and wondering how the story will end, he doesn't know what he's in for. He can't guess that there will be a war-memorial lych-gate any more than North Walsham church knew that its tower and bells would be blown down by a gale.

Me he does not foresee, with my queer craving to revisit the past and give the modern world the slip. Thus we are together—the boy I like to be remembering and the man he might have liked to be with, could he but have known me, his completed self. For the moment, however, he only knows that *The Invisible Man* is what he calls 'triffically exciting', and if I were able to warn him of his future resuscitation by me he would merely be mystified. "What's resuscitation?" he would inquire. And I am not altogether sure that I could tell him what the word resuscitate does mean, in connection with this book. Perhaps I might say that it means 'to imbue one's past life with saturations of subsequent experience'.

Pocketing a few half-ripe filberts for the sake of their past associations, I went warily through the kitchen garden, prepared to transform myself at a moment's notice into an urbanely apologetic stranger who had happened to be in the neighbourhood and was taking the liberty of having a look round after all these years. But there was still no one about, and I went through the door in the wall and across the shady lawn to a seat where I could lean back and light my pipe, listening to the drowsy hum of insects in the lime trees which had grown so tall since I last saw them.

The house didn't seem to have much to say to me now, but as I looked at the lawn, allowing my thoughts to wander where they wished, I found myself remembering Aunt Lula. She had been dead at least thirty years and it was a long time since I had thought of her, and when I did it was with relief that she was at rest—after being so troublesome to her family. Aunt Lula had been a sister of my mother's, unmarried and many years older. She was rather magnificent to look at, and could be quite delightful when she deigned so to be. But—to put it plainly—she had an uncontrollable temper and made scenes in tremendous style. Only too often she did to her family what she ought to have been doing for an admiring public—as a tragic actress. Whenever she felt like it she reduced everyone to a positive pulp, as my mother said. The result was that by 1897 Aunt Lula had for several years been living alone. When she wrote to announce that she was coming to spend a few days with us at Edingthorpe we all knew that before her visit was over there would be ructions.

It was the culmination of those ructions that I now remembered, as I gazed across the lawn at the door which opened from the somewhat comfortless drawing-room where my mother used to sit with a pair of candles burning, at the end of the long noisy days, absent-mindedly re-reading Jane Austen after we had gone to bed. Memory now delineated Aunt Lula, sitting there in the middle of the lawn, on a wooden box which we had been using as a wicket. She was fully dressed for going away, and had just swept out of the house after a one-sided rumpus with my mother. Had Mrs.

Siddons been portrayed seated on a soap-box, her attitude would have resembled Aunt Lula's—majestic, aggrieved, and unbending. Watching her from behind the bushes, I had been chiefly interested in the behaviour of the box, which wasn't in a condition to stand the strain of Aunt Lula sitting, as it were, on her dignity while waiting for Lucy and the carriage to come round and convey her to the station. Needless to say, the box collapsed and with mingled agitation and derision I saw Aunt Lula with her heels in the air and her hat well over her nose. Saw, too, how haughtily she arose and made her exit, round the corner to the front door, disdaining the paltry notion that Emily Eyles might have witnessed the mishap from a window.

It was always like that. Once, when I was quite small, she had stayed at Weirleigh for two or three weeks. She had the Thornycroft talent for modelling, and I used to watch her in the studio while she worked energetically at a bust. I can't remember whom it was a bust of, but it came to a bad end. While she was making it, her face was unruffled and I wished she could always be like that, so clever and entertaining. But when it was finished and a plaster cast had been taken, she flew into one of her tempers and smashed it to smithereens with a hammer, and we all agreed that it was just like Auntie Lula to go and do a thing like that.

Anyhow, when she came to Edingthorpe we arranged a really nice reception for her, hoping that it would put her in a good temper for a time. My idea was to pretend that she was a Plantagenet queen visiting one of her abbeys. She was to be met at the crossroads, and I, of course, was the abbot. My brothers were to be superior monks, and Tessa Gosse volunteered to be a female prior. Busy with my coloured inks, I composed an address of welcome in more or less medieval language. The parson's sermon paper came in useful for this. There were quires and quires of it in a cupboard—faint-lined smooth blue foolscap. It was very enjoyable to write on and had already stimulated my productiveness as a poet, for it seemed to make my thoughts flow more easily than any paper I'd ever known.

Laboriously copied out in pseudo-Gothic characters and plentifully encrusted with sealing wax, the rolled-up address was in my hand when, at the latter end of a muggy afternoon, I mounted my donkey and conducted the procession to the crossroads. I was wearing a painted cardboard mitre and my mother's faded purple cape. My brothers, who were on foot and rather bored with being monks, wore their Scotch tweed cloaks with the hoods up. Tessa Gosse, robed in something friar-like, was doing her best to be realistic in brown-paper sandals. My mother was a mere spectator, with her umbrella up, for it had already begun to drizzle by the time we reached the crossroads. She was joined by some ducks and geese, and a few of the villagers who stood round grinning sheepishly at this queer little performance by the young gentlefolks.

After what felt like a very long time, the shabby old Rectory shandrydan hove in sight, containing Aunt Lula and her luggage, driven by the odd-man (who wore a cloth cap and a livery coat more suitable for a cabman) and drawn by Lucy. My donkey, who liked Lucy, brayed enthusiastically as the carriage came to a standstill.

Aunt Lula, duly prepared for the proceedings by the odd-man, leant back with graciously remote dignity while I dismounted and advanced, rolled-up sermon paper in hand. I had it in mind that Henry III had once visited Bromholm Abbey, whose ivied ruins were only a mile away. Perhaps he had ridden along this very road. So it was fairly easy to imagine that the occupant of the carriage was not Aunt Lula but his Queen. Fixing my eyes on her havocked handsome face under its coils of greying red-gold hair, I reminded myself that this was she for whom we had chanted innumerable orifices—or was it orisons? This was that foreign

Queen whose days had been spent in cold castles with green rushes on the floors and mail-clad knights muttering 'by my halidom' in the corridors, while turbulent barons conspired against the King in other parts of the country. Thus primed up, I read out my abbatical greeting and made obeisance while Aunt Lula pretended not to notice when my mitre fell off. 'We thank you, our loyal subjects,' she replied in her deep and euphonious voice. Whereupon, as it was now raining quite hard, the odd-man set Lucy in motion again and we straggled back to the Rectory.

But all this had been forty years ago, and it was time for me to be going back to the crossroads where I'd left my car.

IX

By the autumn of 1897 my brothers and I had
the reputation of being a bit out of control. Up to
a point our escapades were considered amusing;
but people who stayed in the house must often have
had a headache by the evening. Our behaviour
towards afternoon callers was unreliable, and practical jokes had been known to occur. Dear old
ladies who were staying in Tunbridge Wells during the summer months would drive out to have
tea with Theresa and see her delightful garden
and those jolly boys who had always looked such
little pets in their early photographs. An open
barouche from the livery stables would bring them,
in their best bonnets, along the dozing afternoon
road—just a comfortable hour's drive if you told
the coachman to take the hills at a walk. And then
Theresa's restful drawing-room would receive
them, with its beautifully arranged flowers, and

147

the blue and yellow egg-shell china all set out, with polite little cakes and sandwiches, and the dishes of fruit which looked so pleasant even if one had to refrain from the risk of eating any. And Theresa herself, with her vivacious way of talking, always so forthright and original, would make them feel that they could have driven twice the distance to see her. After tea she would take them slowly round the garden, and would cut them masses of flowers, more than they could possibly put in water when they got home. They would then ask to be shown her studio, and would particularly admire the big picture which she had painted five or six years before, of our Saviour and the little children—a picture which showed us in our angelic childhood and fully deserved their admiration, for it was most touching and beautiful.

But 'the dear boys' themselves, for whom they would now expectantly inquire, would as likely as not be lurking among the laurustinus bushes, grubbily resolved to be ungracious, and possibly regretting that they hadn't arranged the studio skeleton in an arm-chair playing the old Italian lute—a witticism which had successfully startled more than one old lady before now. As for elderly gentlemen, the temptation to squirt them with the garden syringe was almost irresistible. When asked whether, at our age, we were not very tiring and troublesome, my mother usually admitted that she did have a high old time with us. But she ignored all suggestions that it would do us no harm if she sent us off to school. She had a deep distrust of the feeding arrangements at schools, and maintained that as we were all of us delicate it would be a mistake for our brains to be overtaxed by a conventional education. In some ways she was probably right, but by the autumn of 1897 we had begun to need something more strenuous than Mr. Moon, whose curriculum, as he called it, was cautiously proceeding to that terminus when he would have taught us everything he knew. Already we had sometimes suspected that he was swotting things up as he went along.

Mr. Moon had now been our tutor for two years and we were just starting on Euclid and Algebra. It did not strike me as necessary to ask him who or what Euclid and Algebra were. Laboriously learning by heart the definitions of Euclid I resignedly supposed that Euclid was merely the name of something which consisted of unprofitable propositions and diagrams. Mr. Moon never said a word about what geometry really was. Nor did he explain that Euclid was the name of a person. A few years afterwards, accidentally discovering that Euclid had been an old Greek geometrician, I vaguely wondered why I hadn't been told

that before. The information would have made
him a bit more alive, though it wouldn't have made
me any fonder of his propositions. Poor old
Moonie must have breathed a sigh of relief
when told, after we returned from Edingthorpe,
that he was no longer solely responsible for our
education. And we ourselves felt no misgivings
when the German governess, Miss Stoy, came to
live in the house. In fact we at once became quite
fond of her, for she turned out to be a tolerant,
unchivvying sort of person who stopped being
strict as soon as lessons were over. Fraulein was
small and oldish, with shrewd but kind grey eyes
and the complexion of a weathered apple. Her
smallness suited my mother, who used to say that
it was such a comfort to have someone about the
house whom she could look down on; a German
lady perpetually gazing over the top of her head
would really have been rather a trial. Another
thing she liked about Fraulein was that she wasn't
too chatty, and never offered to 'do things for
her'. My mother preferred to do things for herself, and I have heard her say that even if she lived
to be a hundred she would refuse to have a lady
companion or get into a Bath chair. Fraulein was
punctual and methodical; she went her own pace,
like a clock that doesn't hurry. Unobtrusive, self-
contained, and quietly observant, she seldom put

down her knitting, and this automatic occupation
seemed to absorb her into her surroundings so that
she became a comfortable unemphatic presence,
proceeding philosophically toward the next meal.
It is thus that I remember her most clearly, sitting
compact and upright on the drawing-room sofa,
her lips moving silently as she counted her stitches,
her eyes often on the friendly blazing of the fire,
as though she and it were more closely acquainted
than she was with the voices around her. Perhaps
her thoughts were in Germany; but she had been
in England more than half her life, and her old
home in Westphalia, when she spoke of it, was far
away in the past.

After being on our best behaviour with her for
the first week or two, we began to find that when
set on making us do what she wanted Fraulein
was difficult to circumvent. There was my Cod
Liver Oil and Maltine, for instance. At the end
of a meal, having scooped out the inside of a third
orange to her conclusive satisfaction, she would
move sedately to the Sheraton sideboard, uncork
the brown bottle, and bestow on me an uncom-
promising tablespoonful of the cloying nutriment.
No one else had ever detected my habit of holding
the dollop of Maltine in my mouth until I could
stroll to a window and reject it. Fraulein found out
at once; and she always made me stand there till I

had swallowed it down. In more ways than one she got the better of me by her imperturbable obstinacy and artfulness.

Anyhow the large upstairs room in the studio was now our schoolroom, and Moonie was only there in the mornings. Frowsy, as we called her (though she never looked at all untidy), had her headquarters in the old nursery, and there she taught us French and German, with migrations to the drawing-room for music lessons. She took us one at a time, an astute arrangement which enabled her to keep us well under control. Regretfully I remember how little I retained of what Fraulein told me. She was capable, and unwearyingly patient; but I have never found it easy to learn languages—or indeed, anything else. My brain absorbs facts singly, and the process of relating them to one another has always been difficult. From my earliest years I was interested in words, but their effect on my mind was mainly visual. In a muddled way I knew that they had derivations, but my spontaneous assumption was that a mouse was called a mouse because it was mouse-like.

Staring out of the nursery window (from which one got a good view of the rock-garden and my mother, with a flower-pot full of silver sand, wondering whether it would agree with her dwarf gentians) I repeated to myself that the German for window was *Fenster*. Quite an amusing word, it sounded, though it failed to produce a mental picture. But Fraulein never pointed out the similarity of *Fenster* with *fenêtre*, so I continued to think of them separately and only learning by heart prevented me from forgetting both words. Fraulein's teaching was like Mr. Moon's. It lacked illumination. I have a hazy recollection of plodding through a German story about a caliph, while Fraulein told me not to twiddle the fringes of the table-cover. An attempt to make us talk French and German at meals was a pronounced failure. I could have informed a German that the aunt of the gardener had pens, ink, and paper; but after that I should have been hard put to it to continue the conversation without asking to be given pepper, salt, and mustard, or my umbrella.

Music lessons were in a slightly different category to ordinary education, since I really wanted to be able to play the piano properly. For more than two years I went on learning with Fraulein, who made certain that I practised my scales as regularly as I took my Cod Liver Oil and Maline. But my progress was poor, and in the end we both lost all belief that I should ever be able to play even tolerably well. When people came to dinner my brothers could fiddle through their

Corelli and Handel sonatas quite respectably, with Fraulein's capable accompaniment to sustain them. But when it was my turn to perform, nobody could pretend to be enjoying such fumblings, and I was lucky if I got through one of my little Reinecke pieces without hearing Fraulein's lenient voice, from the far end of the room, telling me to begin at the beginning again.

*   *   *

My mother had a strong maternal feeling that I was destined to become a great poet. This feeling expressed itself prophetically when she wrote my name in a copy of Coleridge's *Lectures on Shakespeare* on my third birthday. Let no one suppose, however, that she ever so much as suggested that I should write poetry. On the contrary, she wisely restricted herself to giving encouragement to my childish compositions and reading aloud to me from the poets whom she most admired. She made no attempt to show me off to people.

At the age of eleven I fully shared her belief that I was a heaven-born bard; and by the middle of October I was beginning a new book of poems which would be presented to her at Christmas. My brothers, on the other hand, considered that my talents were overrated. Putting it plainly, they told me that what I wrote was tommy-rot. I don't blame them, for they weren't far wrong. Take the following lines, for example, written during our holiday on the Norfolk coast.

'List ye to the mermaid's song
  Far below in the merman's throng.
  In the rooling (*sic*) sea came the echoes long.
  Deep down below they sang their chant.
  And e'en to land it echoed; and among the trees
  It whispered, and the wandering winds
  Wrote it upon the mellow sands.
  The sea-birds heard it. By the wind 'twas borne
  Unto a place where man has never lived. . . .'

My mother had thought the lines delightful; but Hamo, who had a matter-of-fact mind, remarked that I'd got mermaids on the brain. Everyone knew that there weren't any, and he thought I must be going barmy. With aggrieved condescension I replied that only people with imagination could understand what mermaids meant. There were lots of them in the fairy-story books anyhow, and I liked them much better than his beastly old engineering.

As a rule, however, I wasn't much interfered with when I got out my coloured inks and settled down to embellish the glossy pages of the book whose contents were to give my mother such a wonderful surprise at Christmas. My previous volume had been completed for her birthday about six months before; the new one contained so many leaves that, even though I'd got sixty long-looking 'lines to a stormy night in winter', I was compelled to put in several of my previous poems again, and toward the finish I had to include my prose autobiography of our kitchen cat. There were numerous 'headings and tail-pieces by the author', for I believed in copious illustration, however incongruous. A hop-kiln always came in handy, although in one instance the poem above it was concerned with a soul at the gate of Hades. I drew very badly, but I was fond of the smell of my coloured inks, especially grass-green. When my mother came into the room I told her that she mustn't look: but it was no good saying that to my brothers, who peered over my shoulder whenever they felt like it. On one occasion Michael kicked the leg of the table and made me smudge the wet page with my sleeve. I accused him of doing it on purpose and punched him on the nose. The book is before me now, open at the unlucky page. I had been experimenting with my silver ink, which was never easy to control and took a long time to dry. Anyhow I was contemplating my work with anxious satisfaction, and then, a minute afterwards, I had made Michael's nose

bleed and Emily Eyles was scolding me just as
if it hadn't been all his fault. Sympathetically she
escorted his nose upstairs, leaving me to try and
undo the damage to my book. The first stanza of
'A Vision of Death' was badly smeared, but it is
still decipherable.

> 'So evening fell and everything seemed sad
> And overcome by weariness and gloom.
> Slowly a knight in snowy samite clad
> Was borne away to the darkness of the tomb.'

No one will want to read the rest of the poem, or
any of the others in those two 1897 manuscript
books. But there is one thing about them which
seems worth pointing out. Though written in the
same year they are not executed in the same
style. The handwriting of the earlier volume has a
sort of innocent refinement, and the little decorations are really rather charming. In the later
volume the calligraphy is large and untidy and
the drawings have become crude and insensitive.
The poems themselves, with a few exceptions, are
similarly different. There is a transition from the
serene simplicity of childhood to something uncontrolled, self-conscious, and wilfully lugubrious.
The poetic impulse in me had become more impetuous, while the artistic sense, which so many
children possess up to the age of twelve, was about

to leave me to my own devices until such time as I was old enough to call it back. Meanwhile, not being aware of Nature's arrangements for the artistic development of the species, I continued to think of myself as what I called 'an infant progidy', and if I looked ahead at all I took it for granted that, like little boys who played the piano or violin in public, by the age of eighteen or thereabouts I should be a full-blown performer with at least an epic to my name.

It must be very great fun to be a musical genius and become celebrated at the age of ten, I thought, as I practised absent-mindedly and broke down at the usual place in a Reinecke piece called 'Coaxing Puss' (its German name was 'Schmeichelkätzchen') while one of our cats sharpened his claws on the Spanish leather screen behind the piano. Stopping to munch a half-eaten apple (probably one of those little Golden Knobs which seem to have become extinct nowadays) I decided that being a poet wasn't anything like such an easy career as giving concerts. It seemed to be a sort of double life, in which one was either having inspirations and feeling quite carried away, or else being told not to drop candle grease on the carpet or being reproved for 'making use of such common expressions'. I associated poetic sensations with a rapturous and almost silly solem nity which didn't fit in well with everyday life, and I supposed that grown-up poets lived by themselves and felt inspired nearly all the time. All the great poets I had read properly were dead, and only existed visibly in the frontispieces of their works. I knew very little about their lives, and it wasn't possible to think of them as boys of my own age. My mother had told me that Swinburne, whose poems she hadn't encouraged me to read, was the only important poet now living. She had met him once, at the Gosses', when she was a girl. He seemed to be all head and no shoulders, she said, and kept up a sort of St. Vitus's dance while he talked in a high-pitched voice. She also told me about his kicking a lot of top hats down the steps of The Athenæum because he had failed to find his own. These details made me distrust his greatness. I wished she had talked to Tennyson or Browning instead, though I didn't want to hear that they had spilt a cup of coffee over Mrs. Gosse's best dress, as my mother remembered Swinburne doing. I preferred to think of poets as living in statuesque aloofness. Kicking top hats down club steps didn't seem harmonious.

My own poetical works, as I have already indicated, were becoming noticeably aloof from ordinary affairs. While remaining an optimist outwardly, I was a most melancholy person when putting myself on paper. Eternity and the Tomb were among my favourite themes, and from the accessories of Death I drew my liveliest inspirations. Apart from Posterity, the audience I addressed was my mother, and I didn't want to disappoint her by being insipid and unimaginative.

Even in everyday life she responded readily to sensational news. If there was anything terrible in the morning paper, such as a railway accident, I rushed off to tell her about it. (She usually waited until after luncheon before opening the paper herself.) When the Archbishop of Canterbury was dying I shared her concern with gloating solemnity. Things like that didn't happen every day, and one felt quite important about it.

Toward the end of 1897 my mother took me to London to see the Watts Exhibition. She had known G. F. Watts quite well before she was married. His studio was next door to the house in Melbury Road which Grandpapa had built, and she had often told me how she used to go in and brighten him up when he was feeling tired after painting all day.

Without being altogether aware of it, I had been strongly influenced by Watts's pictures. Large photographs of them were all over the house; there were several in the drawing-room, and I passed Mr. Watts himself (in his self-portrait) every time

went up or down stairs. My brother Hamo was
his godson. I wished it had been me, for Hamo
took no interest in his godfather's pictures and
even treated his second name as a joke, saying that
he ought to have been Hamo What Sassoon. What
I admired about Watts was his loftiness and grandeur. He painted the things I wanted to write
poems about. As a rule loftiness in art was freely
associated in my mind with vast studios where
famous painters, whose names I didn't know,
worked on step-ladders at huge compositions which
had no connexion with what one was accustomed
to seeing in modern life—pictures in which people
wore ample and dignified draperies or else (owing
to living in classical or legendary surroundings)
had nothing on at all. But Watts was different.
There was always a noble idea behind what he did,
and even the names of his works were nearly always
enjoyable. Vaguely impressive and symbolical,
his figures had their existence mostly in spiritual
surroundings; I couldn't say where they came from
and I didn't want to. They made me feel lofty-
minded and ambitious.

Anyhow, to my mother he was 'dear old
Watts': and off we went to London by the early
train, so as to have a good long morning at the
New Gallery. It wasn't often that we went to
London, and people who lived as quietly in the

country as we did had few opportunities of seeing
or hearing anything unusual. In these days, when
children are taken to the cinema at least fifty times
a year, it is worth mentioning that at the age of
eleven I had been to no more than a dozen public
entertainments in my whole life; and the list would
include pantomimes, the circus, Maskelyne's Mysteries at the Egyptian Hall, and Paderewski's
Recital in Tunbridge Wells, which was long before I'd begun to learn the piano myself. My
undistracted imagination had been decently nour-
ished on poetry, fairy-tales, and fanciful illustrations, and my ideas of how people behaved in
real life were mainly derived from *Punch*, *The
Boy's Own Paper*, and F. Anstey's *Voces Populi*.
The Watts Exhibition, therefore, was an excitement, though a serious-minded one. I probably
thought of it as an extra large milestone on my
high road to maturity.

'Won't it be marvellous to see the pictures in
their real colours?' I may have exclaimed while
we were on our way to the New Gallery; for
Auntie Rachel's *Orpheus and Eurydice* was the
only one I had seen, as it were, in the flesh.
Watts had painted portraits of all the famous poets
too, and I was longing to see what Browning
looked like. To tell the truth, the colours weren't
quite what I'd expected them to be. I can remem-

ber feeling slightly disconcerted by their peculiar quality. But although the New Gallery contained such an allegorical assortment of winged figures and ethical sublimities, I accepted them all quite uncritically as works of awe-inspiring genius. That I can still find poetry in those paintings does not seem to me strange. What does strike me as strange is the memory of myself, a dreamy and impressionable child, gazing ecstatically at *The Court of Death* and *Time, Death, and Judgment*—gazing at them with unquestioning delight and going home to try and write poems about them.

X

Restricted though its radius was, I cannot believ
that my existence in 1898 numbered many day
when I complained of feeling dull. I had alway
been a believer in looking forward to something
in the winter I looked forward to spring, and i.
spring I looked forward to the summer, and so or
I seldom began a day without expecting that i
would contain something interesting.

I had already made one notable discovery abou
life, which was that no year was the same as an
of the other ones. From '91 onward, the year:
when I thought about them, seemed like peop
in different suits of clothes: roughly speaking, th
texture of their clothes was the weather. But ther
was more in it than that; they had different faces an
different ways of behaving, as it were. The yea
'98, as I remember it now, was indistinct in ou
line, rather as if Time had taken his eye off m

and was waiting another twelve months before making any serious alterations to my existence. It was the sort of year in which one was allowed to stay up a bit later playing cribbage with Fraulein but nearly always forgot to brush one's hair and clean one's teeth in the morning.

Exhilarating enough it must have been—to be getting up on a fine June day in 1898—to be rushing downstairs and tearing out into the garden before breakfast, listening to nothing, looking at nothing, but just breathing the fresh air and being alive! Merely to think of it makes me feel quite young again, and for a moment I am disknowledged of this time-trod world to which I was then awakening, ignorant of myself and light as the air in which I had sniffed the aroma of frying sausages. God in his Heaven and sausages for breakfast—such must have been the substance of my philosophy as I ran out across the dew-soaked lawn with innocent hopes in my head and the love of life in my heart.

I can't claim that I was always so good at getting up, but for the time being I had a reason for early rising. We had a new horse, and I usually began my days by going down to the stables to inspect him.

During the previous winter my legs had become too long for my dear little black pony. I had shed

tears when he was sold, but his successor was a
real full-sized hunter whom I already looked upon
as my own. Luckily for me, my brothers liked
bicycling better.

My mother was unable to buy expensive ani-
mals. She had gradually sold most of her jewellery,
plus the contents of the plate-chest, in order that
Richardson might always have two horses and a
pony to look after. She had perfect hands and preferred a horse that gave her something to think
about. She and Richardson would go any distance
up to sixteen miles for a day with the hounds, and
they thought nothing of hacking ten miles home
in the dark. The problem of finding a really safe
conveyance for me had caused her to wonder
whether her cat's-eye ring was worth selling. Per-
sonally I hoped she would keep the cat's-eye; for
I was fond of it, and had also rather regretted the
disappearance of my father's brown diamond
which had reappeared in the form of a too good
looking half-hackney who proved to be so lethargic
that he was very soon got rid of at a loss. The new
horse, however, had cost nothing, since he had
been given to us by someone who wanted him to
have a good home in his old age. He was a chest
nut weight-carrier, with three white stockings and
a Roman nose, who had done a lot of work and
was very much over at the knees. But he was s

quiet and sensible that he could almost have taken
me out hunting and brought me back again without my touching the reins.

Anyhow, there I was at eight o'clock on that
summer morning, scampering down the garden
on my way to give Sportsman his lumps of sugar
and ask Richardson to take me for a ride in the
afternoon. For it was a Saturday and there were
no lessons after luncheon. Stopping at the straw-
berry-bed, just to see if many of them were getting
ripe yet, I probably disentangled the usual young
thrush or blackbird from the netting and enjoyed
feeling it struggle from my hand to wing ungratefully over the rhododendron bushes into the wood.
Having done that I was soon down at the stables,
to find Richardson hissing cheerfully away at one
of his horses and the stable boy emerging from the
barn with an armful of hay. The stable boy was
quite a decent cricketer and often came up to bowl
to me when Richardson was too busy to spare the
time. When he heard Richardson go to the corn
bin Sportsman became wildly impatient. It wasn't
safe for me to go into his loose-box when he was
given his feed. 'Someone must have played some
proper dirty tricks on the old chap when he was
young,' remarked Richardson, as Sportsman
rolled his eye savagely round from the manger.
He wasn't ferocious about sugar, however, and

would take a handful of oats quite mildly if one
gave it to him out of doors. But I couldn't stand
there admiring him any longer, as I had to be back
for breakfast.

After breakfast we had an hour of Mr. Moon.
And then, a little before eleven, the stocky figure
of Sergeant Ryan in his respectable blue suit and
bowler hat was to be seen pushing a tricycle in at
the front gate. Sergeant Ryan was the ex-Hussar
who came once a week from Tunbridge Wells to
instruct us in physical training. He was an amiable
reticent man with a small waxed moustache and a
red face which perspired and became mulberry-
coloured when he over-exerted himself. Up in the
top studio we would fall in, wearing our perennial
brown jerseys and corduroy shorts. Idle white
pigeons cooed and scrabbled on the skylight, and
my mother would be downstairs in her studio,
humming to herself, while she worked at one of
the decorations which she was doing for poor
Uncle Don's new music-room. (I say poor Uncle
Don because he was so ill that there didn't seem
much chance that he would ever live in the huge
country house which Mr. Belcher was building
for him.) After a bit she would stroll up to watch
us and say something to the Sergeant about our
taking an interest in our calisthenics. Being shy
and also a little hard of hearing, the first time he

received this remark he gave her a blank look and
mumbled something about none of his family having lived there. My mother left it at that; but we
found out afterwards that he thought she had
asked him if he'd ever been to an inquest at Green-
wich. Phlegmatically he absorbed the word calisthenics into his limited vocabulary and then called
us to attention again. ' 'Ands on the 'ips; 'ands
above the 'ead'. . . . I cannot think of the Sergeant
without those words floating across my mind. And
then I see the four of us club-swinging like a squad
of windmills, after which our exercises culminated
in boxing or fencing. My mother liked the idea of
our being taught to fence, but the masks and foils
were rather wasted on us. The good old Sergeant
did his best for us, with his 'Parrycart, parry-
pierce, parry 'alf-circle, parry secoon', but our
bouts usually lapsed into hits on the legs. Our
attempts at boxing weren't much better. Person-
ally I never could feel that any science was
attached to trying to hit one of my brothers on
the nose. My mother, however, had decided that
we ought to be learning something manly, to make
up, perhaps, for the fact that in 1898 none of us
had ever kicked a football or entered a gymnasium.

After luncheon I got into my brown velveteen
riding suit and waited for Richardson to bring the
horses up to the house. He always made going out

for a ride seem an important event and looked very smart in his livery. He would have considered it a disgrace to have worn his stable clothes when taking me out, and I never saw him drive even a pony-cart without looking as though it was a carriage and pair. Like Sportsman he had perfect manners. When he had assisted me into the saddle, which was rather a long way up, my mother came out with a note in her hand which she wanted him to leave at Major Horrocks's house. I knew already that the note was to say that she couldn't come to tea that afternoon. It wasn't much more than a mile to the Major's; but it was too hot for walking, she said, and if Richardson were to drive her I shouldn't get my ride. I now asked Richardson which way we were going; he suggested that we might go round by Brenchley and leave the note on our way home. There was an all-day match at Brenchley and we could watch some of it over the hedge. This was exactly what I'd wanted. Tom had a way of anticipating one's wishes. So off we trotted, up the hill, in the opposite direction from Major Horrocks's house. At the top of the hill we met a traction-engine, which with some horses might have meant the possibility of tumbling off. But Sportsman passed it as though it wasn't there and I patted his neck appreciatively. Sylvia, a harmless character who usually went in the dog cart, gave a sort of curtsey to the traction-engine, which was politely standing still. As we went along I hoped we should meet somebody who knew me, for I was very proud of being seen on such a big horse. But we saw no one until we got to the cricket ground, except when we overtook the curate, whose opinion I didn't value much, though he always made great efforts to be pleasant. 'He'd look a sight better in that black straw hat without his Monkey Brand beard,' remarked Richardson; to which I callously agreed. A few minutes later we were watching the match; by standing up in the stirrups I could see quite well over the high hedge. Brenchley were batting and the little scoring board on the other side of the ground showed that they had been making plenty of runs. We weren't the only spectators in the road. As usual, the brewer's dray had pulled up and looked like being there for the rest of the afternoon. The drayman, whose horses were half asleep, was watching the game in a heavy indolent attitude which seemed suitable to the barrels of beer behind him, while the youth who drove the baker's van appeared conscious that he ought to be continuing his round though always unable to tear himself away until he had seen what happened next. A little further along the hedge was the tea-tent, which was full of talkative local ladies and would soon contain the curate. Most of the Brenchley players were sitting under the chestnut trees on the far side of the field, and at a respectful distance from the tea-tent was the Rose and Crown beer tent, well patronized by the villagers, one of whom bawled 'Call that ker-ricket!' whenever the Horsemonden fast bowler sent down a bumpy one. Horsemonden being the next village to Brenchley, there was strong local rivalry in the match, and feeling in the beer-tent ran high. Every time one of the batsmen made a good stroke I envied the apparent ease with which he did it, particularly when it was George Collins, who had played for Kent as a professional before I was born and still walked six miles each way to play for Brenchley. When Collins had completed his fifty and the church clock struck four, Tom said: 'We'd better be jogging on now if we're going to leave the mistress's letter at Mascalls.' Reluctantly I rode away, wondering whether *I* should ever make a fifty for Brenchley.

Captain Ruxton's farm was on the hill top beyond the village, and when we got there he was out in the field with his coat off, helping his men to get the hay in. As soon as I saw him I began to wave with my riding-whip, for I was fond of him and he always called me his unofficial godson. Too busy to talk to me, he leant on his hay-rake and watched us go past. Behind him was that wonder-

ful view of the Kentish Weald which one got from
his big meadow, and a good picture of a man of
Kent he must have made as he stood there, in the
prime of life, long before the world became the
troubled place it now is. Farmer Ruxton, his
friends used to call him, and no name could have
suited him better.

It was the sweet of the year, and the countryside
in its afternoon sunshine was like drowsy Elysium,
but my eyes were too young to approach that love-
liness through my mind, and all I thought was that
somehow Captain Ruxton reminded me of a par-
tridge. I couldn't exactly say why; and Richardson
soon recalled me to reality by telling me to hold the
old horse together and not go lounging along with
such slack reins. Trotting on for a couple of miles
we came to Major Horrocks's low rambling house,
which had creepers round its windows and gave
one a feeling of friendliness. As we went in at the
gate I observed that he'd got several people there.
The tea-table was out on the lawn, and the warm
hearted old Major hurried across to greet me.
'Hullo, Fred Archer,' he exclaimed in his throaty
convivial voice. I had a jockey cap to match my
suit, and as I knew that Archer had been a famous
jockey, I felt pleased by the salutation. But I became
shy and awkward when the others crowded round
me, patting Sportsman's Roman nose and making

jokes, which I didn't think funny, about his way of standing with his knees bent forward. Major Horrocks himself wasn't much of a rider, anyhow. Captain Ruxton had a story about how they'd once gone out hunting with the West Kent together. The Major had tumbled off at the first jump and remained recumbent until he'd been given a good dose of brandy. So when he went too far by saying that my mount looked a bit lonely without his cab I felt inclined to ask him if he'd been out with the West Kent lately. But he soon put things right by making me get off and go and have some fruit-salad out of a large bowl. And then his sister, who was stone-deaf and much older than he was, and wore a poke-bonnet, led me away to the lily pond where I helped her to feed the goldfish with breadcrumbs. There were crowds of them and they were very large. Owing to her deafness Miss Horrocks's voice went quavering up and down in the queerest way; but not being able to answer her made it quite easy to be with her, and I was always vaguely impressed by having heard that she had once been kissed by George the Fourth (whose face I associated with a four-shilling piece which had been handed to my mother in a shop when she was being given change for a sovereign).

Major Horrocks had a lovely garden and grew all sorts of things which no one else had got. Pointing her stick at a flowering shrub, Miss Horrocks told me that it came from the Caucasus and had been introduced into England by one of the old gentlemen at the tea-table, a club friend of the Major's who had been all over the world finding plants for people's gardens. When she took me back to the table I sat gazing at him with discreet curiosity, wondering whether he travelled in the clothes he was wearing now. He was tall, and wore loose lavender-coloured trousers and patent leather button boots. A little further up one came to what looked like a buff evening waistcoat. He had a rich red tie with a ring round it which contained a sort of fossilized beetle, and his dark jacket had a brown velvet collar. When I ventured to look at his face, his pale blue eyes met mine with an amused expression in them. 'Sizing me up, eh? Well, and what do you think of it all, my boy?' he inquired, fanning himself with a wide-brimmed grey hat which had I Zingari colours round it, though I didn't know what the ribbon was then. I could only smile shyly; but I was thinking that his crisp whitey-gold beard went very well with his rig-out, and that his voice was more like being read aloud to than talking. I now add that he had the look of an eccentrically distinguished connoisseur—the sort of elderly gentleman who is incomplete without an intaglio ring.

By now I had begun to need relaxation from behaving with decorum, so I wasn't sorry to rejoin Richardson and feel natural again. As soon as we were out of the gate I told him about the old codger who'd been to the Caucasus. I couldn't say for certain where it was but I intended to find out on one of Moonie's maps. Meanwhile we were on the dull bit of road from Paddock Wood, but half-way up the hill we overtook the carrier's van which brought our parcels from the station. Homewood the carrier always kept wicket in the matches on our village green. While Tom was telling him about the Brenchley and Horsemonden match I wondered whether he'd got our box of books from Mudie's Library; it didn't seem quite polite to ask him, though. When helping my mother make the last Mudie list I had put down *Under the Red Robe* by Stanley Weyman, with two crosses against it to show that it was really wanted. So after seeing Sportsman unsaddled I hurried up to the house. By then the box had been delivered and I was able to pounce on my Stanley Weyman before one of my brothers bagged it. Tea was going on in the dining-room. Sitting on my book, I bubbled over with information about everything that had happened to me since I last saw them, while Fraulein knitted and my mother occasionally told me that I should ruin my digestion if I ate so fast. After

tea my brothers refused to play cricket and returned to their workshop, so I went off to the
fort, with *Under the Red Robe* under my arm. I
had made up my mind to try and read it slowly,
which I'd never yet succeeded in doing with Stanley Weyman's books, for they were so exciting
that one simply gobbled them, especially when one
got near the end.

The fort had been built by my brothers, with
amateur assistance from me. It dated from the
previous autumn, and stood on a bank in the
wilder part of the garden, most of which could be
overlooked from its roof. For the fort had two
storeys and was nearly fifteen feet high at one end.
It had started as a low shanty among some old
laurels and the second storey had been interwoven
with them and the middle branches of a mountain
ash. Poles, planks, sheets of galvanized iron, and a
disused cucumber frame had gone to its making.
The second storey was a cabin with one small
window and the cracks filled up with putty. To
get on to the roof one clambered up a ladder fixed
to the outside. There was a little windmill which
clattered merrily while the whole edifice creaked
and swayed with the trees, so that we felt as though
we were on a ship.

Now that I come to think of it, the fort was not
unlike one of the above-ground dug-outs I was in

during the war, except that it had no earth on the
top. But it was constructed to keep out nothing
more dangerous than grown-ups, and the only
shooting we did was with seed potatoes hurled
from sharp pointed sticks, aimed at the gardeners,
or even at Fraulein, when we saw her cruising
along the lower lawn with her crochet-work and
couldn't resist a long-distance shot at her. Sitting
in the cabin after dark during the winter with a
couple of candles guttering, we felt very snug and
independent, though smoking home-made clay
pipes filled with tobacco from my mother's cigar-
ettes hadn't been much of a success. One day I'd
had a bright idea and daubed the inside of the
cabin blue, red, and yellow, with oil-paints from
her studio. Afterwards I wished I hadn't, for the
smell of paint became monotonous.

By the summer of 1898 the fort had reached a
state when there seemed nothing more to be done
to it in the way of improvements. My brother
put up a lightning conductor, but after that they
ceased to use the place much and I often went
there when I wanted to be alone and feel poetical.
Sitting on the roof now, with my chin on my
knees, I gazed across the valley and lost myself
in a daydream about becoming the G. F. Watts
of poetry and making centuries for Kent and exploring the Caucasus and having romantic adven-

tures like the hero in a Stanley Weyman story. Better than it had ever been before, summer was around me to be accepted by my senses like a vague thought of familiar happiness. Haphazard as the architecture of the fort were my reasonings about life, and most of my beliefs were founded on misunderstandings. But the blue evening distance was beckoning me beyond those few known miles which ended, more or less, with the Medway, and after that became imbued with the magic of ignorance, like the names of places which weren't merely railway stations along the line. There was Snodland, for instance—a village I'd only heard of, though it was less than fifteen miles away. The name of Snodland made me think of its inhabitants as always sitting in a huge oast-house, half stupefied by the fumes of drying hops, talking in blurred voices and dressed like the peasants in a German fairy-story. Such place-names were like the titles of certain books on the drawing-room shelves. I had often looked at the backs of such books, without ever bothering to open them, because stories of my own were produced by their names. *Green Pastures and Piccadilly* was one; and *My Husband and I*, by Tolstoy, was another, though that one created a gloomy impression, since it made me think of my father and mother being unhappy together, and I dimly won-

dered why the word husband always felt so sad.
Anyhow, some day I would bicycle miles out
beyond Maidstone and discover what was there;
and then the blue distance wouldn't seem so far
away, or give me that funny heartache feeling
which I couldn't understand. Beyond the garden
and the wood below it, and across the valley, were
those distant hills; and the future seemed to lie
beyond them. It was from there that visitors came
to see us, out of their far off lives which were so
unknown and interesting, like things that happened in books. . . .

Emerging from my meditations, I overheard
the uneventful sounds of that June day which was
now drawing near to sundown. I heard my brothers
hammering in their ivied workshop, and the shouts
and pan-beatings of a bird-scaring boy in the
cherry orchard across the road, and the persistent
voice of Fraulein calling one of the cats.

After that I get one more memory of myself, at
the very end of the day. I am in the bedroom which
I no longer share with my younger brother. I have
been forbidden to read in bed and many a time in
the past my candle has been taken away from me.
But I have provided myself with a surreptitious
night-light, and by its flickering glow I am steadily
reading *Under the Red Robe*. As soon as I hear my
mother coming briskly along the passage I blow

out my night-light and hide it under the bed-clothes. But she passes my door and I hear the handles of her dressing-table drawer rattling in the next room. And then I don't seem to be wakeful enough to begin reading again. To-day's happenings move indolently across my mind, gradually becoming blurred and topsy-turvy. Very gently the night air stirs and sways the tall white window curtains, bringing the surf-like sound of a train going along the valley. Leaving behind it silence and profound peace, the train seems to be carrying me with it into the land of Nod.

XI

To explain the topography of a garden distinctly
is a difficult thing to do, unless one is tediously
elaborate. I am aware that no reader, however
conscientious, could as yet make a map of the
Weirleigh garden, or even find the way from the
house to the alcove between the potting shed and
the vinery. Guidance being needed, let me lead
my reader out of the drawing-room by the glazed
door: going westward across the lawn, we leave
the studio on our left; the lawn slopes to a cedar
where we turn to the right and stroll down the
Peony Walk which goes between my mother's
finest flowers and rose-bushes and comes to an
end at the alcove. The alcove is of red brick with
Virginia creeper all over it and contains a white
painted seat. There had been a Jenny Wren's nest
there every year since I could remember.

Twelve months have passed since the end of my

previous chapter and we are in the middle of a
warm lazy afternoon, lulled by the sound of the
mowing machine's long unbroken journeys as the
fat pony pulls it up and down the lawn. At this
point the word *we* ceases to signify reader and
author, and becomes my brother Hamo and myself
sitting in the alcove with our tutor Mr. Hamilton,
who had now been with us more than a month.
(Michael, at the mature age of fourteen and a half,
had been sent to an advanced co-educational school
and was spending his first term finding out that he
'would rather be somewhere not so cranky',
which resulted in his being transferred to an ordinary preparatory school in the autumn.) Luckily
for us, Mr. Hamilton was a perfectly conventional
tutor. To begin with, he had been in the Rugby
eleven, which was in itself enough to win him my
undiluted admiration. At Cambridge he had cap-
tained his college and made some centuries. In
addition to these credentials he was consistently
good-natured, tactful, and modest. After tutoring
us for a year he intended to start learning to be a
clergyman, and in the meantime he occasionally
practised intoning the service in his bedroom.
Tall, clean-shaven, and rather stylishly dressed,
Clarence Hamilton had completely eclipsed poor
old Mr. Moon, whose lack-lustre pedagogics we
had altogether outgrown. Fraulein still remained

with us, but her stolid lessons were now subsidiary
to Mr. Hamilton's refreshing routine. Compared
with him she was only a harmless appurtenance of
the household, giving the cats their milk and trying
to teach me the piano.

I now felt that at last I had some chance of
catching up with all those other boys who had
been normally educated since they were eight or
nine years old, thereby getting four or five years
start of me. By the time when we are discovered
sitting in the alcove, we were just beginning (outside lesson hours) to call our tutor 'the Beet',
which was an abbreviation of 'Beetroot' and referred to his rather ruddy complexion. But as a
rule our behaviour was so respectful and obedient
that he accepted the nickname with his usual bland
good humour. Wholesome and energetic, the Beet
was thus an entirely suitable person to liberate
us from the localisms of our over-prolonged
and somewhat segregated childhood. He was, of
course, aware that my mother regarded me as a
poetic genius; but my ecstasies and inspirations
were already evaporating some time before he
arrived, and in his presence I couldn't help feeling
that writing poems was a rather priggish occupation. Poetry was, however, included among our
studies. We learnt by heart Tennyson's *Revenge*
and *Defence of Lucknow*, and read aloud the

first Canto of Spenser's *Faerie Queene*. That sort
of thing was quite enjoyable in the schoolroom,
but I preferred keeping my favourite poems to
myself. Learning the *Ode to a Nightingale* as a
lesson would have been distasteful; to have begun
telling the Beet that my heart ached and a drowsy
numbness pained my sense as though of hemlock
I had drunk might have made both of us feel a
bit silly.

For Mr. Hamilton's batting average I felt an
eager and almost proprietary concern. He began
by knocking up a dashing thirty in an important
Brenchley match. Richardson, who was captain of
our rustic team, expected much of him, and I
myself had hopes of seeing him make at least fifty
in his first match for Matfield. But fifties, as I well
knew, were seldom made on Matfield Green; in
fact when I'd played there for the first time, a few
weeks before, the other side had been all out for
thirteen, though I'd scored eight runs myself,
owing to them bowling underhand at me. Mr.
Hamilton, indeed, seemed none too sure about his
fifty when he was putting on his pads to go in first
wicket down after Richardson had won the toss;
he was aware that the mown piece in the middle
of the Green looked better than it really was. The
turf was quite decent, but when people ran about
on it there were hollow-sounding thuds, almost as

if there was a cellar underneath. In dry weather the wicket could without exaggeration be described as dangerous, and Mr. Hamilton was about to bat on a very dry wicket indeed. 'Which cap are you going to wear?' I inquired, as he rummaged in his bag for his batting gloves. For he was both a Butterfly and a Crusader, and I was wondering which colours would be likely to overawe our opponents most. But one club cap was much the same as another to the opposing players, several of whom had both braces and belts to sustain white trousers which were so high in the waist that, as a local humorist remarked, they 'looked as if they cut 'em under the arms'.

The game now began, and some lively hits into the rough grass were made off the old-fashioned round-arm bowling. It took a long time to get into double figures at Matfield unless you skied the ball, and scientific strokes along the ground only resulted in singles. Would C. H. Hamilton's batting be too stylish for the Green? I speculated, when the first wicket had fallen and he was wending his way toward the crease in his Crusader cap. The question remained unanswered, for his actual bat played no part in the proceedings. The bowler, who had grim black whiskers and very long arms, took two steps up to the wicket and delivered a fast ball which rose sharply and

whizzed past C. H. Hamilton's nose. The next
ball did the same but struck him in the ribs. The
third one never rose at all. It shot under his bat
and knocked his middle stump down. 'Them toffs
never do no good on the Green,' remarked a
bandy-legged old labourer who was standing behind the scorer's table. Quite pleased about it, he
seemed, though I eyed him angrily. In consequence
of this and a few somewhat similar experiences,
the Beet decided that he preferred playing for
Brenchley, and did so with gratifying results. He
made sixty-four in the Flower Show Match. Meanwhile he lit his pipe with an air of relief rather than
regret that his innings was over so soon.

Authentic details of the distant past being difficult to recapture, I take this opportunity of relating
that Mr. Hamilton's pipe reminded me of an
episode in his University career which he had
amusingly described to me. One day he was in
G. L. Jessop's rooms; for that famous man had
been a college friend of his. Jessop's pipe—a large
one—had become clogged, and he was blowing
into it for all he was worth. Mr. Hamilton, with
sympathetic interest, was looking over his shoulder. The climax came, and a clot of tobacco flew
into one of his eyes, causing inflammation for some
days afterwards. In my opinion, however, there
was nothing inglorious in having tobacco blown

into one's eye by Jessop, who hardly ever played in a county match without smiting at least one ball clean out of the ground. Anyhow, the anecdote has stuck in my mind, so I see no harm in repeating it.

*   *   *

Thus another summer slipped away, and although we may have been a bit troublesome at times it was generally agreed that the new tutor had improved our conduct quite wonderfully. Visitors marvelled at our meek behaviour at mealtimes, and my mother often asserted that Mr. Hamilton was the staff and prop of her existence. Not many weeks after the staff and prop had returned from his summer vacation, the Boer War broke out and everybody began to read the newspapers with grave and anxious faces.

Just before war was declared our Uncle Don died. He had been ill for about two years, and his new house still stood uncompleted among his woods and fields, on which, from his Bath chair, he had gazed with such life-loving eyes. Mr. Hamilton took us to the funeral. Uncle Don had been greatly beloved by all who knew him, and when I saw his coffin on the farm waggon drawn by four of his favourite Clydesdales I experienced a sort of dumb dejection which had nothing to do with the mock mournfulness of my poems about death and the tomb. Very subdued and insignificant I felt, as I looked upon the reality of grief in the stricken faces of my cousins, on that quiet sunless October afternoon when all speech except the service was a muffled undertone, and in an interval of silence I heard the slow shuffling feet of those who carried their heavy burden into the church.

*   *   *

Although the phrase *fin-de-siècle* had, so far, failed to catch my eye, toward the end of that year I heard, as a matter of course, quite a lot about 'the end of the century'. The great argument about it between Fraulein and the Beet, which began amicably enough, ended in their being, for the time being, barely on speaking terms. For this the German Emperor was entirely to blame. He had announced that the new century wouldn't really begin until the 1st of January 1901, and Fraulein, refusing to believe that he could be wrong about anything, supported him with bigoted pertinacity. Mr. Hamilton, who shared the national indignation against the Kaiser for telegraphing hearty congratulations to President Kruger because the British were doing so badly against the

Boers, was fully in favour of starting the new century a year earlier. Just as they looked like losing their tempers at luncheon the controversy would close down, only to begin all over again next day. The final result was a stalemate, but arguing continued up to the actual chronological crisis. On New Year's Day Mr. Hamilton, who had spent Christmas with us and was just off for his holiday, beamingly inquired of Fraulein what the Kaiser was proposing to do about babies born in Germany during the year 1900, as they couldn't begin to be alive before next January. Fraulein gave no sign of having heard him. She had made up her mind that she was still knitting in the old century, and Mr. Hamilton made no further attempt to convince her that she wasn't.

During December, my brother Hamo and I celebrated the advent of the new century ourselves by making a big bonfire. To begin with, I had opposed the idea because it meant pulling down the fort, which had enough tarred timber in it for a very fine blaze. I was fond of the fort, and at first I did my best to save it. Hamo, however, was determined to destroy it, for he thoroughly enjoyed strenuous occupations, such as chopping or digging. He had built the fort affectionately, and was now longing to tear it down again; in fact he'd already borrowed the garden hatchet and

190

crowbar for the purpose. 'Anyhow,' I said, 'you can't do it without my permission; it belongs to me just as much as it does to you, and Michael ought to be asked about it as well.' 'What'll you take for your share?' he asked dourly. Knowing that he'd got ten bob, I became irresolute, and after a brisk haggle, agreed to take 7s. 6d. It went without saying that he was entitled to his share of any chocolates I bought with the money. Michael, who was still at school, wasn't consulted at all.

Before Hamo began demolishing it, I got Mr. Hamilton to photograph the poor old fort, with me standing on the top. By next day nothing of it remained except a few sheets of galvanized iron lying about among the laurels.

Thus, between tea and dinner on a dry frosty evening, the fort went up in flames and in brief glory was consumed. In the heat of the moment I was too busy and excited to connect the conflagration with anything except the new century. But even if I'd stopped to meditate, I don't suppose I could have realized that the sparks were flying upward from those few years of the departing century which I was able to remember. Incorporated in the fort there had been a few planks which had formerly belonged to the first 'Build', which we children had constructed in 1893. This being so, I might well have fed the bonfire with many another relic of the past, such as our dapple-grey rocking-horse, and the babyish books from which I had first learnt to read, and the old Ariston organ, whose muffled grunting music had expired several years ago when the handle came off and nobody bothered to get it put on again.

BOOK II

SEVEN MORE YEARS

I

When Michael returned to school, for the first summer term of the new century, Hamo and I went with him, for our first term anywhere. The school was only fourteen miles from our house, and had been recommended for us by Fraulein, one of whose best pupils had been there. She frequently sang the praises of Mr. Norman, the headmaster; and Michael (who alluded to him more familiarly as 'Cockeye') brought home very favourable accounts. So we went there with the comfortable knowledge that The New Beacon was a 'jolly decent' school to be at, though we couldn't believe that any of the masters were as nice as our Mr. Hamilton.

Naturally, it took some little time to get accustomed to being there. Quite well I can remember now, having just arrived, I stood alone on the edge of the playground, feeling newer than I'd ever done in my life as I watched some other boys

whose treble shoutings sounded so clearly on the
brisk air of a fine end of April evening. I was much
larger than most of them, which made me seem,
for the moment, acutely inexperienced and help
less. Then a bell began ringing, and while they
were crowding in for tea Mr. Jackson, the chief
assistant master, came to my relief with an en
couraging smile. 'Cut along now and get yourself
some grub. Feeling a bit hollow inside, aren't you?'
he exclaimed in his pleasant voice, and made me
seem not quite so new. From that moment I liked
Mr. Jackson very much. He was less formidable
than Mr. Norman, though I afterwards liked him
just as much, in a different way.

After existing for many years in Sevenoaks, the
school was beginning a thriving career on higher
ground about a mile from the town. The new
buildings had been finished six months before, so
this was only their second term. I associate my
first evening with a smell of freshly painted corri
dors and class-rooms, the noise of scurrying feet
on bare floors, and a general sensation of echoing
emptiness and vociferation among which I was
speechless and unconfident. I felt as if I had left
all my private life at home and must in future do
most of my thinking aloud. My play-box, with my
name painted on it, had been dumped down in the
gym and the only life I could now call my own

was, so to speak, inside it, along with a large tin
of mixed biscuits (some of them with sugar on the
top) and other personal property.

Meanwhile I had on my mind a single problem
from which there was no escaping. Its cause was
neither complicated nor uncertain, and merely
amounted to this. My mother had sent Hamo and
me to school without any shirts. Misled by her
loyalty to 'thick warm woollen underclothing', she
had provided us with starched 'dickeys' to our
Eton collars and nothing else. It seems odd that
Michael, whose garments were normal, hadn't
drawn attention to the deficiency. But he had overlooked it; and I suppose it was characteristic of
me that never having worn a shirt before, except
in cricket matches, I took it for granted that I
could do quite well without one at school. I probably wondered vaguely whether it was all right
and then hoped for the best. (Hamo didn't bother
much about how he was dressed.) It was only when
I was up in the big dormitory that my sense of
humiliation became complete. This, I felt, was
something which I should never be able to live
down. It was bad enough to be, for my age, only
half educated. To be only half dressed as well was
the finishing touch. Unconsoled by observing that
at any rate I wasn't the only boy who didn't wear
pyjamas, I hastened into my nightgown and said

my prayers. (Hamo, who was in another dormitory, was probably quite unperturbed.) Next day I managed to get dressed without anyone noticing anything wrong. The crisis came in the middle of the morning when there was half an hour's break for cricket practice. I was eager to show Mr. Jackson that I could play quite decently, but it wasn't possible for me to bat 'in my shirt-sleeves'. When it came to bowling, the weather being rather warm, he asked why I didn't take my coat off. My embarrassment enabled him to discover what was amiss, and he led me and Hamo off to the matron, who supplied shirts from somewhere. After that I became a different person, and felt that I really was 'Sassoon minor' instead of being a secretly shirtless absurdity.

*   *   *

Next term I was 'Sassoon major'. Michael had gone on to Malvern, whence he remarked casually in one of his letters that he had 'been to play the violin to an old chap called Elgar'—this being the result of my mother having eulogized his fiddling to his house-master. But the 'old chap' (who was then forty-three) found it impossible to take him as a pupil.

As 'Sassoon major' I became a more or less

ordinary boy, impulsive, irresponsible, easily influenced, and desirous of doing well at work and games. Before long I was known as 'The Onion', which implied that I was a bit 'off my onion'; so I suppose that I wasn't considered altogether prudent, though no one suspected me of having written poetry in past years. I now looked upon that as an occupation to be almost ashamed of. Occasionally, however, I had a feeling that I had lost something wonderful which I still wanted, though I couldn't remember what 'feeling inspired' had felt like. Queen Victoria died, but I never even thought of celebrating the occasion in verse, though I got the giggles when Mr. Jackson sat on his bowler hat at the memorial service.

I enjoyed being at school, and did quite well at cricket, which was what I was keenest on; and my mind was kept busy by the process of making up for the lost time of my much retarded education. If I could walk into that mind, as it was in the latter part of 1901 when I was in my fifth term, I don't think I should discover much to write about. Supposing it were a Saturday evening during the roasted-chestnut season, I should be sitting in the big schoolroom; Mr. Norman would be reading aloud to us while the boys at the desks around me crackled chestnuts with such effrontery that at last he would shut the book (which was, I

think, *Moonfleet*) and warn them that 'unless you
little toads stop making so much noise' he would
discontinue there and then. As a rule there was
spellbound silence while he read, for he did it
splendidly, but roasted chestnuts had on this occasion competed successfully with the breathless
excitements of *Moonfleet*. I didn't eat them myself,
not being fond of chestnuts, and also because I had
become rather dignified during my final term. For
I was now turned fifteen, and Mr. Norman had
taken to treating me as a person to be relied on.
It was nice to be trusted like that, and I felt quite
sorry to be leaving. Next term I should be at
Marlborough, where I should have to begin all
over again and not be relied on at all. Anyhow I
was grateful to Mr. Norman for having, with some
difficulty, persuaded my mother to allow me to go
there (though he hadn't been too pleased when I'd
scribbled off my entrance exam paper in such a
hurry, because the questions had seemed so simple
—in fact he'd been obliged to make me do the
Latin prose all over again, cutting out the 'nomi-
native absolutes', and I suspect that he suppressed
the earlier version).

If that 1901 mind of mine could revisit me now
it would, I am sure, contain much unformulated
thankfulness to Mr. Norman and Mr. Jackson for
the way they'd helped me to catch up with my

school work. Even then I realized that 'Cockeye'
was a magnificent schoolmaster, and when he was
in a benevolent mood I felt that I would do anything for him. He had a nickname for most of us
and just lately he'd taken to calling me 'Dook Sig'
because my deportment had become so dignified.
'Now then, Dook,' he would say, 'are you ready to
repeat your hundred lines of Hecuba yet?' For he
had promised the school an extra half-holiday when
everyone in the top form had done it. But as I'd
only begun to learn Greek about a year before, the
parrot-like performance was keeping me awake at
nights. After six weeks of mute gabbling I did
manage to get through it without a mistake, but I
was last by a fortnight and the first line, 'Lady,
methinks you know the will of the people' ('Gunai,
lokō men s'eidenai gnōmēn stratou') has been
heavily engraved on my memory ever since, and
I never shared Mr. Jackson's ardour for Euripides.

Of Mr. Jackson himself I was very fond. What
a ripping time we'd had when he took a party of
us on the Norfolk Broads last holidays. (My mind
would contain a spontaneous renewal of the smell of
soles frying in the cabin of our boat, and perhaps a
memory of the spacious solitude of Hickling Broad
on some quiet September evening with a yellow
sunset flaming beyond the reedy margins.) Mr.
Jackson was such a good golfer too—much better

than Mr. Norman, who sometimes looked rather
red and angry when he topped his drives. Only
that afternoon I'd had the privilege of caddying
for him; he was playing against the old Earl on
the nine-hole course in his park near-by. It was a
treat to watch Mr. Jackson's tee-shots. After I had
sponged and wiped his ball (a brand new 'Ocobo')
and placed it deferentially on his meticulous modi-
cum of sand, he addressed it with solemn deftness:
after a series of graceful waggles his club climbed
majestically to the top of the swing —as though
the whole world was watching it—paused for a
fraction of a second, and calmly descended to that
crisp click which sent the ball far down the fair-
way, beginning low and soaring a little toward the
end of its flight. How I wished I could drive like
that; for I had taken up the game with enthusiasm
and particularly liked it because I could practise
by myself. The Earl didn't drive very far, but he
had an old wooden putter with a long head with
which he trickled the ball up to the hole very art-
fully. This afternoon he had given me half a crown
because Mr. Jackson (who gave him a stroke a
hole) had just beaten him on the last green, and
was wondering how much of it I would spend next
time the grub-cart came. The grub-cart came once
a week; it was pulled by a weak-looking pony
steered by the squeaky-voiced local confectioner

Most of the boys met it at the gate, clung on and formed a queue, and trotted along behind until it drew up. No one was supposed to spend more than a shilling, but I should probably spend the whole of the Earl's half-crown, unless all the Turkish Delight had been sold by then—for I had long since given up trotting behind the cart, owing to having become so Dook-like, and always waited until the unseemly scramble was over.

Meanwhile Mr. Norman is still reading *Moonfleet* to his now chestnut-abstaining audience. But the ruminator who has been sitting in that schoolroom is a very 'old boy'—five and thirty years or more removed from the 'Beaconian' who will be a 'new boy' at Marlborough next term. To see myself as I really was I must look at a photograph of Mr. Jackson and his class. I am standing behind him, and beside me are those two nice German boys, first cousins, who afterwards fought against one another in a war which neither of them wanted. My own face confronts me with an expression of amused simplicity, suggesting that I wasn't bothering about anything that might be happening when was fourteen years older than the photograph, taken one Sunday morning in bright winter sunshine, to remind me long afterwards of these precariously remembered humanities which my soliloquies recreate.

*   *   *

The year 1902 began with snowy weather, which meant lots of tobogganing on tea trays down the steep field outside our garden. My mother joined in with gusto; but one afternoon, when the sport was in full swing, the parlour-maid brought out a telegram and handed it to her over the hedge by the apple house. Mr. Beer was dead, and Auntie Rachel wanted my mother to come at once. Brushing the snow off her hat she hurried indoors. During the past two or three years Auntie Rachel had become more and more vague and peculiar. She had sent me a review copy of a volume called *Bibliography of the World's Municipal Literature* last Christmas, and altogether one could never be sure what she would do next. We had long known that Mr. Beer's death would be a happy release, but now, in that cheerful snowscape, we stood and wondered if we ought to go on with our tobogganing. The slide was in splendid condition, and it might thaw by to-morrow; and after all we hadn't seen poor Mr. Beer since about 1897. Hamo suggested tossing up, but none of us had got a coin, so we resumed operations, feeling sorry for Auntie Rachel and rather hoping we shouldn't have to attend the funeral. We did; and the house in Chesterfield Gardens, never a festive one, seemed as though it had been waiting all its life for this mournful event. Auntie Rachel, when we got a glimpse of her, was murmurously distraught, and seémed to have ordered a vast quantity of white flowers which no one knew what to do with. Very few people were there, and most of them were strangers to us. We drove to Highgate Cemetery and back, leaving Mr. Beer's coffin in the handsome private mausoleum which his father had purchased for himself and those who came after him. There was a subdued grimness about the ceremony which made me unable to relax into feeling reverent. I knew that Auntie Rachel had been behaving very oddly. Since he died she had been continually telling my mother that Mr. Beer wasn't dead, and at intervals she had protested against his being buried at all. My mother, who had shown her usual ability to deal with an emergency, had been through a very trying time since the telegram was handed to her over the hedge.

The only comforting thing about it all was that in his last moments Mr. Beer had recovered consciousness and thanked everyone around him for their kindness. For many months he had lain speechless and inert, but at the end he was his old self again, gentle, charming, and charitable to the world which had endowed him with great riches and the feeble constitution which had made his last years a living death.

II

I felt pleased and rather important about going to Marlborough. I knew that I couldn't do brilliantly either at work or games, but I was determined to be industrious. I had no idea what it would be like. I merely saw myself against a vague background of the public-school stories which I had read, and went rapidly on to the moment when the head-master was bidding good-bye to me at the end of my career. 'Well, Sassoon,' he would say, 'superlative scholastic ability isn't everything in the battle of life. Your sterling qualities of character have been an influence for good which I shall not readily forget. Thank you, my boy. I am proud of you.' Something like that may have passed through my mind, as an antidote to the discomforts of a vaccinated arm which had 'taken' only too well; but when I was at last actually on my way to Marlborough I had some difficulty in preventing my heart from sinking into my boots.

To make matters worse, my mother had insisted

on going with me. I knew that it was only natural that she should wish to do so, but it would have been easier if she had contented herself with seeing me off at Paddington. I could then have settled down into being numbly nervous. As things were I was obliged to keep up an elaborately cheerful demeanour while feeling rather as though she were taking me to my own funeral.

Unpunctually early, we arrived at Marlborough about midday, and rumbled up from the station in a cab to call on the headmaster, a silver-bearded old gentleman who received my mother with beautiful courtesy and told me to be a good boy with an air of having said it so many times before that he wasn't expecting to be aware of my existence again. Canon Bell, who was now within eighteen months of retirement, had been there for more than twenty-five years, and looked so venerable that it wasn't easy to imagine him doing anything else (which was, of course, an incorrect impression). Feeling unnaturally good, I left his presence without having uttered a word. And that was the only chance I ever had of talking to 'Tup', as everyone called him, for short. My mother thought him a perfect old dear, and I was much relieved that she managed to refrain from drawing his attention to my exceptional intelligence and unrobust constitution.

A few minutes later our cab deposited us at the door of Cotton House, which was my real destination. Everything was very quiet, as the other boys didn't arrive until late in the afternoon. We were shown into the study of Mr. Gould, my housemaster, who looked more like a retired military man than I'd expected. But perhaps that was only because he had a majorish moustache. To be strictly accurate, he looked like an easy-going clubman who had put away a good deal of port in his day.

Polite but unvolatile, he conducted us over the house, replying as best he could to my mother's anxious inquiries about everything connected with the preservation of my health. What must he be thinking of me? I wondered, as I followed them round, and my mother asked whether there was any chalk in the drinking water. When we came to the dormitories and she informed him that of course I'd brought my own blankets, I felt that I'd rather have had no blankets at all than be made to look such a milksop. Mr. Gould appeared to be the sort of man who would much prefer to be reading a French novel in his armchair instead of listening to all this fuss about what was the most sensible diet for growing boys, but I could see that he thought her an original character. Our tour of the premises ended when, with a slight ▟▛ of

elief, in which I joined, he left us at the green
baize door of the matron's room. I didn't so much
mind my supposedly delicate health being discussed with the matron—a prim but very nice
person who seemed more gratified than otherwise
by my having brought my own blankets. Like
many people who met us for the first time, she
evidently assumed that we were some of those
rightfully rich Sassoons who were always entertaining Royalties. As we weren't, it would have
suited me better, for the time being, if my name
had been something more like Tom Brown. I knew
only too well what a nuisance it was to have unusual names, and how funny everyone would be
about it. Before I was much older someone would
be calling me 'Stinkweed Bassoon'; I had no illu-
sions about that. But if the idea of conversing with
people who had met the Prince of Wales appealed
to the matron's imagination I see nothing unnatural
in it. A house-matron's life is not a socially eventful
one. From Miss Boult, at any rate, I never afterwards received anything but kindness and good
manners, and I only wish I could have enlivened
one of her dull hours by describing how the Shah
of Persia had once stayed with us at Weirleigh. In
the meantime she gave me some caps to try on and
when I had selected one that fitted me and had
been warned not to wear it on the back of my head

I felt a little less unprepared for public-school life
My mother said it suited me much better than my
billycock, and Miss Boult, whose heart she had
entirely won, directed us to the Ailesbury Arms
where we had a large but unfestive lunch.

With a forlorn access of affection I saw her off
at the station, promising to wear my warm over-
coat on all possible occasions. With an unsympa-
thetic whistle the little train disappeared down the
branch line to the junction, carrying away from me
that loving heart, whose anxieties and agitations I
was too young to accept with responsive understanding. My devotion to her was so comprehen-
sive that I had never given any thought to it. I
merely took it for granted that we were necessary
to one another, looking forward to the time when
I should be grown up and able to share my freedom with her, and repressing the hateful idea of
her becoming less young for her age. But I did
wish she wouldn't be so fussy about me; and it
was a sort of relief to be alone with what was ahead
of me as I walked away from the station, which
was a single-line terminus, and felt like it. Marlborough itself looked a nice enough place, with
its wide High Street and old-fashioned houses
and Mr. Gould had seemed quite a decent old
chap. But when I passed the college gates again I
was heavy with heart-sinking despondency about

that immediate future in which I alone could prevent myself from exposing my ignorance of all the
things which a public schoolboy ought to know. I
had always been bad at finding out how to behave,
and here I was, without a friend in the world
except the matron, who would be no use at all
when all those other boys arrived.

It was a grey windless afternoon, mild for the
time of year, so I wandered up the hill to the edge
of Savernake Forest. Sitting on the dry turf of an
ancient earthwork, I gazed pensively at the smoke
going quietly up from the red roofs of the town
below. After a while I bethought me of a bar of
chocolate cream which I'd got from a penny-in-
the-slot machine at the railway station. Nibbling
it slowly, I derived such consolation as I could;
and then returned stoically to Cotton House.

The safest thing to do, I thought, was to try
and be as silent and inconspicuous as I could. This
wasn't difficult, for the other boys were too busy
with their own concerns to take much notice of
me, and I was far too shy to ask anything. There
was nothing wrong with my clothes, anyhow. I
was rather pleased with my grown-up looking
black jacket. My stick-up collar, however, had
caused me a lot of worry ever since I put it on for
the first time when leaving home. It was a stiff
double collar, and after fixing both sides of it to

my front stud much manipulation seemed to be needed before I could get my tie into it. Apparently one had to push the tie up with one's fingers but mine could never make it stay inside all the way round. Grubby marks appeared on the collar too, and it went soft in places. For the first two days I walked about wondering whether I should ever learn how to do it properly and envying the way other people managed to get their ties up to the top of their collars so nicely. It seemed a great stroke of luck when at last some good-natured youth gravely showed me how to do it. It hadn' occurred to me that there could be any other method except mine, and altogether it was quite a good example of my lack of practical ingenuity.

The first time I got up to go to early school was flustered from the beginning by frenzied attempts to inveigle my tie into my collar with cold fingers. It seemed as if I were in a buzzing existence where everyone was bumping about and slamming doors and all noises were unnaturally loud and essentially uncharitable. Since no serious work had been done on the previous day I had only been to the Upper Fourth form-room once to have school books doled out to me, and every thing had been so confusing and strange that I had failed to take adequate observations of my sur roundings. So now, emerging into the dark winter morning, I was acutely uncertain whether I knew where my form-room really was. Hurrying up the road to the fateful tolling of the bell I had an indistinct idea that after going in past the porter's lodge one turned to the left and went up some stairs about half-way along the quadrangle. Everyone else seemed to be flitting by in business-like haste and I didn't like to ask my way. After I'd been up one wrong flight of stairs the bell stopped, and I realized that there was now nobody to ask. I was alone in the gas-lit corridor of a nightmare, where all doors were shut and everyone except me safely inside answering their names. Half my wretched tie had got outside again and if ever I found the right door I should have to go in at it with the whole lot of them grinning at me.

In this awful moment a belated master, enormous in cap and gown, came bustling along and I managed to ask him the way to Mr. Meyrick's form-room. To him I was merely a new boy with a scared white face and a crumpled collar. But for me the whole episode, including my ordeal of entering that droning classroom late and out of breath, remained for fully twenty years afterwards in my repertoire of unpleasant dreams, in spite of the fact that, like most of our poor little mistakes in life, it only ended in my being told not to do it again.

Seven More Years

★　　　★　　　★

One afternoon during my first week I went to
see 'old Bam' about my music lessons. 'Bam' was
Mr. Bambridge, the organist, who for many years
had been an affectionately regarded institution
both in the college chapel and outside it.

With my music under my arm I made my way
to his house, which was at the edge of the town,
just beyond the little Kennet. Leaning over the
bridge to give my mind a few minutes' rest by
listening to the river, I wondered how much water
would gurgle under the arch before I had acquired
control of the organ. It seemed a very large instrument for me to tackle, considering how poorly I
played the 'Venetian Gondola' piece in Mendels-
sohn's *Songs Without Words*. But if I couldn't
make a piano sound eloquent and spirited (as the
piano tuner did in between the dull parts of his
work) how could I hope to produce magnificent
noises from an organ? It must feel fine to be able
to do that, I thought, as I stared vacantly at Savernake Forest up the hill—and then just saved *Songs
Without Words* from falling out of my 'kishe'
into the Kennet. (For the benefit of non-Marl-
burians I must explain that a 'kishe' is the flat
cushion which the boys fold around their books
and sit on when at their work.)

Before ringing the bell I put my tie straight and

214

thought what a relief it had been when I discovered the correct way to get it inside my collar. Mr. Bambridge, whose lean figure and bearded face I had already caught glimpses of in chapel, greeted me with bluff geniality. More than that, he looked at me as though I was an object of interest, which no one else at Marlborough had hitherto done. A spectacled lady was standing by the piano, and she too eyed me with what seemed like expectant curiosity. A slight wave of uneasiness passed through my system. Could it be that they believed me to possess musical ability? My apprehensive feeling increased when 'Bam' produced a letter which I recognized as being on Weirleigh note-paper. 'Well, my boy,' he remarked in his bass voice, 'your mother writes that you have a real love of music. Let's hear what you can do.'

The sequel needs no elaboration. Too nervous and flurried to play it even tolerably well, I created an immediate fiasco with the 'Venetian Gondola Song', and was thankful when they stopped me half-way down the first page. Real though my love of music was, I had been unable to give them any audible proof of it. With a twinkle in his eye Mr. Bambridge laid aside my mother's letter and arranged the time of my first organ lesson.

Hurrying back to Cotton House to change for hockey, I wondered whether I should ever feel a

success at anything. Not at hockey, I feared, for
in that game I seldom ran more than a few yards
with the ball before someone hooked my stick and
took it away from me.

Except for morning chapel, the only occasion
when the whole school met together under one roof
was the middle day meal, known as 'Hall'. Boys
like myself who belonged to one of the 'out houses'
associated very little with those who were 'in College'. One felt that they lived a different sort of life
and were nearer to the centre of things—the centre
point being, of course, the venerable 'Tup'. To
begin with, 'Hall' seemed rather impressive. One
heard, from far away at the high table, the Latin
grace pronounced by one of the school prefects—
those sauntering potentates who wore white ties
on Sunday and read the lessons in chapel as though
they'd forgotten what it was to be a boy. When we
all sat down the hush was inundated by a confused
hubbub and clatter and jingle which, when first
heard it, made me feel that the Marlburians as a
whole were something very imposing. Mr. Gould
had a habit of coming in late. I suspect that he
preferred an early luncheon at home, for he restricted himself to cheese and conversation while
sitting at the head of our table. Sometimes, as he
passed along to his place, he would stop suddenly
and concentrate his disapproval on someone o

whom he had received an unfavourable report. On the day after my interview with Mr. Bambridge, while dubiously consuming some beef which was rather a queer colour ('College meat' in those distant days was notoriously bad and often had magenta blotches on it) Mr. Gould astonished me by giving one of these choleric performances of his. Flabbergasted me, in fact, since it was upon me that he swooped. The combination of my affluent surname with my mother's solicitude for my health had imbued him with an idea that I was one of the pampered rich and rather a soft sort of boy into the bargain. I became overwhelmingly aware of this when he seized me by the shoulder and shook me violently, exclaiming, in a voice which was somewhere between a bay and a bleat, 'So you play organ, do you, you wretched fellow, you play organ! I know why you play organ. You play organ to get out of playing games, you wretched brute!'

Considering that I'd got a nasty bruise on the shin playing hockey on the previous afternoon, his onslaught seemed jolly unfair; so I replied, with tremulous resolution: 'No, sir, I don't. I want to learn the organ, but I don't want to get out of playing games.'

This somewhat appeased him, and he moved on, amid the suppressed merriment of those sitting

around me. But for the remainder of the day I felt
aggrieved and indignant at his ungenerous impu-
tation that I was the sort of boy who would rather
play 'The Lost Chord' than get his house colours

*   *   *

Mr. Gould's annoyance about the organ lessons
turned out to have been a blessing in disguise, for
it had created quite a good new Gould joke. So far
I hadn't learnt half the members of my house by
name and had only got to know a few of the younger ones to talk to. Nobody else had done more
than give me a casual or incurious stare, except
when some lordly youth shouted 'Fag' and told me
to fetch something for him. During the next few
days, however, several of the Olympians took
notice of me, though their attentions consisted
only in gazing at me with mock solemnity and
then saying in sepulchral tones, 'You play organ.
No reply was expected; but it made me feel less
lonely and inferior.

Soon afterwards I had a further opportunity of
being modestly conspicuous.

Late one afternoon the rather pudgy-faced lad
who played the piano at evening prayers entered
my study to tell me that as he'd cut his finger
badly I'd got to play the hymn tune that night.

protested that I wasn't nearly good enough to do
t, but he assured me that no one would mind a bit
f I made a few mistakes, and I was unwillingly
persuaded to experiment with the piano. After
hearing my rendering of 'Lead, Kindly Light' he
decided that I was quite capable of acting as
accompanist, and, having chosen what he considered an easy tune, left me to rehearse it at my
leisure on the ancient upright. 'You needn't worry
about the words. The loud and soft bits don't
matter,' he remarked, adding: 'It's Saturday, and
Gould always has an extra glass or two of port that
evening, so he won't be particular.' I observed
with relief that the hymn had only five short verses,
and after playing the tune through about a dozen
times I seemed to have mastered it, though I still
felt that I should break down owing to nervous-
ness.

Anyhow, at nine o'clock I was duly seated at the
instrument with my back to the audience, which
included, of course, the matron, who always sang
the hymn as if her genteel voice had been looking
forward all day to its bit of exercise.

Like one in a dream I waited. Then Mr. Gould
came through the door of the library which was
between his part of the house and ours. After reading out one or two routine notices, the head of the
house handed him the usual slip of paper with

the number of the hymn on it, and we amen'd our
way onward toward my part of the proceedings.
After 'Lighten our darkness, we beseech Thee, O
Lord', Mr. Gould, rather as though he were thinking of something else, gave out 'Hymn number
four hundred and fifty-seven'. With fingers which
felt as if they belonged to someone else I executed
my solo, unconvincingly, but at any rate correctly.
The worst was over, it seemed, for I should now
have the support of some sixty throats, including
Mr. Gould's husky baritone and the matron's
pious alto. Almost without waiting for my timid
accompaniment the house came to my aid in whole-
hearted harmony. In fact they surprised me by the
hosanna-like loudness of their singing.

> 'How blest the matron who endued
> With holy zeal and fortitude,
> Has won through grace a saintly fame,
> And owns a dear and honoured name.'

Preoccupied as I had been by my responsibilitie
as a musician, I had altogether overlooked the
facetious interpretation of the words. And even
now, as I struck the first chord for Verse 2 (which
began 'Such holy love inflamed her breast') I could
only confusedly suppose that I had somehow blun-
dered when Mr. Gould practically bellowed 'Let
the music cease!' After an irreverent silence, our

house-master, since it was his duty to do so, asked the Almighty to grant us in this world knowledge of His truth and in the world to come life everlasting. When all was over and we had risen from our knees, he made a bee-line for me and was evidently about to shake me till my teeth rattled. But my horrified countenance must have made him think again and realize that the forbidden hymn had been chosen for me. So he changed his course and merely stopped on his way out to exclaim from the library door to those who had not already made themselves scarce, 'You brutes! You wretched brutes!'

Good old Gould! Successive generations of Marlburians took him for granted as a person whose oddities of behaviour were there to be made fun of. But he had much in him that was kindly and gentle, and his not infrequent explosions meant little more than that a lifetime of schoolmastering had shortened his temper and impaired his digestion.

Every night after lights out he went round the dormitories with a shaded candle. One heard him approaching with his short shuffling steps, and sometimes, as he tilted his glimmer of light on my upturned face he would mutter 'Good night, you Siegfried.'

That night he paused for a few seconds longer

than usual by my bed but said nothing, for I was
pretending to be asleep. But as he passed on I
heard him chuckling to himself.

Marius Herbert Gould was more of a Herbert
than a Marius, though a first-rate classical scholar
and a bit of an epicure about food and wine and
life in general, as befitted a club-loving bachelor.
He never struck me as being very spiritual; but if
from a better world, he ever revisits this one, I can
well imagine him taking up his flat candlestick to
go the nightly round of his old house, murmuring
as he toddles from cubicle to cubicle, 'Ho, you big
fellow', or 'Hullo, you little fellow', to the uncon-
scious successors of those whom he had thus addressed in bygone years. Anyhow, if his ghost were
indeed able to return, it would have the satisfaction
of knowing that it need not get up next morning
to mount that ladies' machine of his, with its high
handle-bars, and bicycle up the Bath Road to meet
the Middle Fifth at early school.

In conclusion I must add that he was the most
aloofly unhastening cyclist I have ever seen. A
sedate walker could almost keep pace with him.
Boys overtaking him would sometimes call out
from the footpath, 'You're scorching, Mr. Gould.'
To which he would quite genially reply, without
turning his head, 'Shut up, you wretched brute.'

Seven More Years

By the time I was almost half-way through my first term I felt that I was getting on much better than I'd expected. No one seemed to have taken an active dislike to me and I was in Mr. Gould's good books through being so high in my form that I was nearly certain to be moved up next term. But there had been a long spell of bitterly cold weather and it was not unlike a rest-cure when I found myself in the sanatorium with an attack of measles. More like ending as a permanent rest-cure, it became, when measles was followed by double pneumonia and I ceased to be clearly aware of what was happening around me. This submergence occurred after a sleepless night during which I couldn't make anyone hear me and became so thirsty that I was reduced to drinking out of my tepid hot water-bottle. By next morning everything was blurred and chaotic. I was dimly conscious of my mother standing beside my bed, and again she was there, giving me beef-tea out of a feeding bottle. Later on she reappeared with a large kind bearded man who listened to my chest but seemed a long way off. (Everyone in the sanatorium except me knew that this was Sir Thomas Barlow, the famous physician, who had been telegraphed for by my mother soon after she arrived.) I was told afterwards that I had been so ill that I was prayed for in chapel, which was very gratifying. The headmaster might not remember who I was, but he had prayed for me by name, anyhow and I felt none the worse for it.

My mother, however, had done something more nourishingly helpful. Having seen my condition and sampled the sanatorium beverage which called itself beef-tea, she went briskly off to the Ailesbury Arms, ordered beef-steaks, and descended to the kitchen where with her own hands she concocted some of the strongest beef-tea ever made in Marlborough. To this day I don't know for certain how many steaks she got the goodness out of, but imagine that the feeding bottles from which I dreamily imbibed contained the essence of about half an ox. Her activities were, I believe, considered a bit *infra dig.* by the authorities. Parents of apparently good social position didn't do such things as a rule. But she undoubtedly kept my strength up and when Mr. Gould visited me, early in my convalescence, he said, 'Well, you Siegfried, your mother is a wonderful woman. I am not at all sure that she didn't save your life.'

For several weeks I remained a contented invalid, but by the end of March I was at home again firmly resolved to start practising cricket as soon as the weather was good enough.

*   *   *

At the beginning of May I returned to Marlborough feeling far less of a booby than I'd done in January. In addition to my six weeks' pre-pneumonia experience as a Marlburian I now had my brother Hamo with me, and he was so much more self-possessed and sagacious than I was that it was an obvious case of two heads being better than one. My initial advantage over him soon disappeared; he went his outwardly imperturbable way without seeking advice from me or anyone else. There was little likelihood of Hamo ever making a fool of himself, and his presence would make all the difference if I had any troubles of my own.

On the whole, however, that term was a fairly comfortable one for me. Nobody expected much of me, so I felt that I was doing quite decently, especially when I took seven wickets for eighteen in a Lower Game House Match. Also I had climbed out of the Upper Fourth, and my new form-master, Mr. O'Regan (who had played hockey for Ireland) was so easy to work for that I felt like remaining with him as long as I could.

One trivial dilemma of mine during that summer insists on being remembered and recorded. Anxious to show voluntary keenness in every way I could, I joined the Rifle Volunteer Corps. I still

possess a black button with a bugle embossed on
it which reminds me of my *café-au-lait* coloured
tunic with blue facings, the small forage cap worn
on one side of the head, the cartridge bandolier,
and the black leather gaiters which came about
half-way up one's calves. The old carbine which I
carried was always rather an unknown quantity to
me. I ordered, shouldered, and presented it to the
best of my ability, but I never felt that it was my
best friend, as a soldier should. A few rounds of
blank were all I fired from it. For precautionary
reasons, the bayonet was an absentee.

Only about a third of the school belonged to the
Rifle Corps, and I sometimes wondered why I had
joined it myself, since it was obvious that I had no
prospect of getting into the Shooting Eight and
going to Bisley, and I had never regretted that
wasn't old enough to be out in South Africa fighting against the Boers. But the dilemma which I am
about to describe was caused merely by my being
told to 'go and fire Morris tubes on the indoor
range'. What exactly was a Morris tube, I wondered, vaguely supposing it to be some sort of
cartridge. And what chance had I of doing anything with a Morris tube except make myself look
silly? The longer I put it off the less I liked the
idea, but I had to go in the end and the sergeant
instructor seemed moderately pleased to see me

Another boy was there already and I watched him fire his ten rounds and hit the target nearly every time. The target was only about fifteen yards away, but to me, when I lay on my stomach squinting along the barrel, it appeared to be a very small piece of paper indeed and the bull's-eye only there to make fun of me. After a series of experimental explosions I breathed freely again and hoped that something lucky had occurred. But it hadn't. Scrutinizing my target, the sergeant-instructor found it entirely unperforated. Unnecessarily puzzled, he told me to try again, watching me more closely this time. Before I'd fired another shot he exclaimed: 'Why bless me if you aren't shutting the wrong eye!' Further attempts resulted in my hitting the paper once and being told that I should never make a marksman. Should I make an organist either, I wondered, as I went across the quad to the chapel, turned on the hydraulic blower, and began to practise pedal notes.

Playing Handel's 'Largo' with my fingers and the *vox humana* stop out was all very well, but my feet steadily refused to learn how to find their way about the lower regions. I mention this because it was an example of my life-long inability to do two things at once. Anyhow the reposeful emptiness of the chapel was a much needed contrast to things like the indoor rifle-range, and many an afternoon

hour I spent there, blissfully alone with my rumi
nating mind and experimenting with the stops
until, perhaps, dear old 'Bam' strode in and told
me to cease fooling about and practise properly

But I must get back to Pat O'Regan's ground
floor form-room, and it is on a Sunday evening in
the summer that I choose to return there. Sunday
was a day on which I wondered what was happen
ing at home and felt more human than on week
days, when everything was such a scramble.

My Sunday letter to my mother has been written
since tea, and I must remember to post it, for it is
still in my pocket. Out in the empty quad, twilight
is falling. The boys around me are listening con
tentedly while little Pat O'Regan, at his high desk
reads to us with his pleasant Irish articulation
'You are brave. For my sake do not be rash!' That
is how his voice returns to me; for he was giving
us, with subdued gusto, the bit about the young
lady and the curate in *The Golden Age*—a book
which gave me a pleasant feeling of being away
from school and doing things one wasn't allowed
to in a shady garden with lots of good places to
hide in.

Sometimes he read us a little poetry, and when
we had an odd twenty minutes to fill in he would
if the spirit moved him, tell us to write some our
selves, and offer a prize of half a crown. Than

you, Mr. O'Regan, for those half-crowns (I nearly always won them). You were the only person at Marlborough who ever asked me to write poetry. The first time I won the prize you had my verses framed and hung them in the form-room, so for the sake of old times I will reproduce them here:

> My life at school is fraught with care,
> Replete with many a sorrow.
> When evening shadows fall I dare
> Not think about to-morrow.
>
> The extra lesson doth correct
> My wandering attention;
> And other things which I expect
> It might give pain to mention.
>
> But extra lessons cannot kill,
> And blows are not so hard
> That they will end the life of this
> Ambitious little bard.

Though much less likely to win half-crowns, my private versifications at that time were more ambitious—portentously solemn, in fact. I remember being inspired to dirge-like depths by the illness of King Edward VII which caused the postponement of his Coronation. I also wrote an ode on the death of King Richard II. After being dormant for three years the poetic impulse had returned to me. Without any mental ingenuity I was blundering back into my earlier ecstasies, when 'feeling inspired' had been like taking a leap into space and I felt that I must express the inexpressible or burst in the attempt. My reawakening came quite suddenly, in the early part of that summer. I was alone in the library of Cotton House. Idly I pulled out a book, which happened to be Volume IV of *Ward's English Poets*. By chance I opened it at Hood's 'Bridge of Sighs', which was new to me. I had always preferred poems which went straight to the point and stayed there, and here was a direct utterance which gave me goose flesh and brought tears to my eyes. It wasn't so much the subject of the poem which thrilled me as the sense of powerful expression and memorable word music. For the first time since I had been at school I felt separated from my surroundings and liberated from the condition of being only a boy. As a child I had believed in my poetic vocation and had somehow felt myself to be a prophetic spirit in the making. Now my belief was renewed and strengthened. Down the steps on the other side of the door was the hall with its cricket and football teams painted up on the walls. I should never be at the top of any list of names down there, where I could hear the house factotum laying the tables for tea. Down there was an unprivileged nobody. But up here, with this book in my hand and this poem in my head, I was alive with some power which I would some day put into words. And those words I would find, said I to myself, that the spirit within me might be made manifest.

III

My third term at Marlborough came to an end
several weeks sooner than it ought to have done.
All I need say about it is that the simultaneous
effort of trying to get to the top of Mr. O'Regan's
form and doing my best to find out how to play
'Rugger' proved too strenuous for my constitution. By the middle of November this had become
obvious to Mr. Gould and the matron, and I was
packed off home with a strained heart and both
eyes bunged up by ophthalmia. By the time Hamo
came back for the holidays I was feeling more like
myself again, but the family doctor had forbidden
me to play ping-pong or walk upstairs, and I began
to feel that my public-school career would never be
anything to write home about. Laboriously though
I had been memorizing the ingredients of education, I never clearly understood what I was learning, and my mind was incapable of taking clever

short cuts to higher things. Meanwhile I had
finished with football until next autumn, but a
slight kink in the bridge of my nose was there to
remind me that someone had tried to drop a goal
with a sodden ball and had flattened out my face
instead.

So I didn't really mind much when the doctor,
well backed up by my mother, decided that it
would be highly imprudent for me to risk returning to school for the Lent Term. Faced by the
prospect of existing for two or three months before
I could play golf, ride a bicycle, or even get on to
a horse, I had a bright idea and became a book-
worm. Until then I had only collected modern
books with coloured illustrations and most of these
had been Christmas presents. I now set to work to
amass a real library—the sort of library in which
one went up a ladder and pulled out a dusty volume, to discover with delight that it was a first
edition of somebody like Bunyan.

By a stroke of luck I got hold of a current
number of the *Bookseller's Circular*, in which that
fraternity advertised their second-hand wants and
offers. For the present all that I wanted was their
latest catalogues, and I communicated with about
half a dozen of them *per diem*, hoping that they
would be favourably impressed by our crested note-
paper. Catalogues poured in by every post, and I

perused them with sober excitement. Some were
manuscript lists from more or less private persons
whom I had mistaken for shops. Others had full
page illustrations and came from firms who were
asking prices like £500 for a single volume. As
my capital at the moment was only one pound, and
my aspirations unlimited, the obvious thing to do
was to exchange some of the books which were
already at Weirleigh.

What I aimed at was a large cosy accumulation
of leather-bound tomes. The smell of such books
appealed to me and suggested leisurely lives in
days when authors had odd handwriting and did
their work very slowly in panelled parlours while
their wives made home-made wine or sang sweetly
to the lute. I wanted my books to be as old as
possible or else to be mentioned in Mr. Gosse's
History of Eighteenth Century Literature, which was
my sole guide to what was worth getting out of
catalogues.

My next problem was to find out whether any
of the booksellers wanted any of the several hundred books, most of which had belonged to my
father, and were in the big white-painted cupboard
in the studio.

Thankful for anything which would keep
me occupied, my mother offered no objection,
merely putting in a plea for what was in the

drawing-room, especially her gardening books.

Out in the studio, with the *Bookseller's Circular* in one hand, I soon discovered a 'first edition wanted' in Gissing's *New Grub Street*. This being a mere three volume novel in a shabby green cloth binding, I wasn't particularly optimistic about it; but Brownish Bros. of Birmingham were, and I got a flying start by being allowed 35s. in books for it. I followed up this success by being allowed 30s. (also in books) by W. Jiggle (also of Birmingham) for one of Walter Pater's. Subsequent transactions were recorded in a diary, whose accidental preservation enables me to quote a few specimen entries.

January 15. Heard from Brownish Bros. They are willing to give £1 5s. in cash for Gissing or £1 15s. in books. Have decided to accept the latter alternative, so wrote immediately for *The Works of Samuel Johnson*, 12 vols., calf, 1801, 15s.; Sir Dudley Digges's *State Letters*, folio, old calf, 1665, 5s.; *Paul and Virginia*, 12mo., calf, 1799, 2s.; Potter's *Euripides*, 2 vols., calf, 1814, 5s. 6d.; and the *Life of Queen Elizabeth*, 4to., panelled calf, 1738, 3s. 6d. This leaves 3s. to my account.

January 16. Heard from Jiggle. He allows £1 10s. for Pater's *Appreciations*. I therefore order Rollin's *Roman History*, old calf, 8vo, 10 vols., 5s. 6d.; *The Works of William Penn*, folio, old calf, 1776, 8s. 6d.; *The Life of Frederick II*, 5 vols., half calf, 1780, 1s.; Bacon's *Sylva Sylvarum*, folio, old vellum, 1669, 10s.; and *Burke on the Sublime*, calf gilt, 1812, 3s. This completes the 30s. for Pater's *Appreciations*.

January 20. In the afternoon drove to Tun. Wells and went to Chapple's (quite good shop). Bought Moore's *Lallah Rookh*, 8vo., 1822, 2s.; Cowper's *Poems*, 2 vols., 12mo., 1800, 2s.; Pope's *Rape of the Lock*, sm. 8vo., 1798, 3s.; and the *Miseries of Human Life*, 12mo., 1807, 1s. The first three in nice bindings. Cowper is old green calf. *The Miseries* a bit worn and covers of *The Rape* slightly loose.

January 21. Nothing happened.

January 22. Brownish Bros. write saying they have dispatched *S. Johnson* etc. by goods train, but *Paul and Virginia* is sold. I therefore tell them to send Adam Smith's *Wealth of Nations*, 3 vols., full calf gilt, 1791, 5s.

January 23. Collected thirty books which I do not want and only encumber the shelves (including Lane's *Arabian Nights*, *The Life of Ole Bull*, and *Precious Stones and Gems*, all of which are Wanted) and sent them off to Brownish in a box (by passenger train, carriage paid).

January 24. Received books from Brownish and also Jiggle. *Queen Elizabeth* rather dilapidated. Has one side off and title-page loose but can be mended. *Fred. II* also poor. Others good. Rollin has nice red labels. *Penn's Works* 1771. Large thick folio. About 1 foot 4 inches by 10 inches. A success.

January 26. Received from Jobson Ltd. *Faithful Character of Charles I*, 1660, 2s., and Archbishop Usher's *Annals of the World*, folio, 1658, 1s. Shall send back the *Character of Charles I* as it has back off. Usher seems a bargain. Large bookshelf was put up over bureau in my room.

Thus and thereafter I accumulated volumes and arranged them affectionately on my shelves. I also wrote to the Army and Navy Stores for some burnishable gold, with which I brightened up the tooling and added lustre to the lettering of the labels. But although I found serene satisfaction in gazing upon their serried backs (especially by firelight when the wind was rumbling in the chimney) I cannot say that the insides of my antiquated acquisitions made much impression on my mind. Rollin, in spite of his 'nice red labels' proved utterly unreadable; Digges and Usher were dull companions for a long winter evening; and I found the *Works of William Penn* impenetrable. I soon stopped trying to follow *Burke on the Sublime*, and Bacon's *Sylva Sylvarum* turned out to be less attractive than it sounded.

In a list of 'Books read in February' I find some

Shakespeare plays, several of Johnson's *Lives of the Poets*, and various eighteenth-century poets (as recommended by Mr. Gosse's *History*). At the end of the list is Hume's *Treatise on Human Nature*, from which, I am quite sure, I derived no enlightenment at all. Most of my serious reading was undoubtedly done with my watch on the table, and my thoughts must often have wandered away to the golf links over at Sevenoaks, where I should soon be well enough to go and have a game with Mr. Jackson. With him I was continuing my classical studies by correspondence—making rather heavy weather with Horace and Sophocles.

But what about the 'ambitious little bard'? you ask. What was he doing with his vocation while liberated from his life at school which he had, poetically, described as 'replete with many a sorrow'? Let us consult that diary and look for clues. On the title-page we find his name stamped in purple ink. This was the result of his having answered an advertisement headed 'Earn Money by Writing'. Not without hope he sent off a preliminary 1s. 1d. as requested, and received, by return of post, a rubber stamp with his name on it, plus the information that for every rubber stamp he sold he would earn threepence. This wasn't at all what he'd expected, but the stamp came in quite useful, though the ink ran when he tried it on his cricket bat. In addition to the book-buying campaign, the diary contains little except golf scores and details of games played in at school, but on some blank leaves at the end he has copied out Hood's 'Bridge of Sighs', 'Rugby Chapel' by Matthew Arnold, and Byron's 'On this day I complete my 36th year'. After that come twenty-four lines of his own, 'An Allegory, written Jan. 1903', in which Youth makes a six-stanza journey to Old Age, the moral being that 'Time's golden sands run all too fast'. This appears to be the only symptom of poetic activity until I discover, on April 4th, a cryptic entry, 'Heard W.A.B. Acc. E.I.'

Was W.A.B. a second-hand bookseller, you wonder. No, he wasn't. He was Mr. W. A. Bettesworth, the editor of *Cricket; A Weekly Record of the Game*, to which I had been a subscriber for two or three years. Eager to get into print, I had already sent several poems to *The Marlburian*, but it had ignored them. Why not try *Cricket*, I thought—any sort of print being preferable to none. At that time the question of altering the height of the wickets was being widely discussed, so I sat down and composed a parody of 'The Sands of Dee', named it 'The Extra Inch', and posted it off to Mr. Bettesworth, whose office was in Upper Thames Street (which suggested that he

did his editing in a punt while doing a bit of
angling). To my surprise and delight he accepted
it, politely adding that *Cricket* did not pay for
poetry. And why should it, when I would willingly
have paid Mr. Bettesworth (who had played for
Sussex) to print it? As this was my first public
appearance as an author I will reprint 'The Extra
Inch' (with apologies, not only to the late C. Kings-
ley, but to the reader).

'O batsman, rise and go and stop the rot,
  And go and stop the rot.
  (It was indeed a rot,
  Six down for twenty-three).
  The batsman thought how wretched was his lot,
  And all alone went he.

  The bowler bared his mighty, cunning arm,
  His vengeance-wreaking arm,
  His large yet wily arm,
  With fearful powers endowed.
  The batsman took his guard. (A deadly calm
  Had fallen on the crowd.)

  O is it a half-volley or long hop,
  A seventh bounce long hop,
  A fast and fierce long hop,
  That the bowler letteth fly?

The ball was straight and bowled him neck and
  crop.
He knew not how nor why.

Full sad and slow pavilionwards he walked.
The careless critics talked;
Some said that he was yorked;
A half-volley at a pinch.
The batsman murmured as he inward stalked,
"It was the extra inch." '

There are periods in an autobiography when it is
best to be on the safe side and allow oneself to be
lost sight of for a bit. Rather than risk wearying
the reader with insignificant reminiscences I will
therefore pass quickly over my last four terms at
Marlborough. Although I got along fairly comfortably, it was mainly a matter of staying on there
till my time was up. As a cricketer I was merely a
respectable member of the House eleven for a
couple of summers. As a conscientious but confused ingredient of the 'scrum' I was awarded my
House colours, which I earned more through dis-
comforts endured than actual merit. As a hockey
player I did not exist, because I was again kept at
home for the Lent Term (this time as a precaution
against contracting pneumonia). While at home I
was rather tepidly tutored by a reticent young man

from Oxford, of whom I remember nothing remarkable except that he read solidly through al
Scott's novels without any outward sign of invigora-
tion. My own leanings toward literature receivec
recognition at Cotton House on one occasion only
when I was with some difficulty persuaded tc
recite a poem (which was chosen for me) at the
annual House 'Leaving Supper' in 1903. To ?
select and fully fed audience in the squash racque
court I gave a very indifferent performance o
Thackeray's 'When Moonlike ore The Hazur
Seas in soft effulgence swells', and no one mindec
in the least when I broke down in the middle anc
had to refer to the book.

My last year was spent in the second division o
the Lower Fifth, which was exactly half-way u;
the school and felt as though it was as far as
should ever get. During the summer term of 190.
my form-master became tolerant of my semi-idle
ness. My taste for elaborate calligraphy amuse
him, and I always copied out my weekly Lati
prose exercise in pseudo-Gothic characters wit
ornate initial letters in red ink, though he vetoe
my suggestion that I should try a bit of gildin；
But by then it was obvious that what I did or le
undone made no difference to me or anyone els￼
for I had no future as a Marlburian. I couldn
have stayed on for another year even if I ha

wanted to, since I wasn't in a high enough form
to avoid superannuation at the age of eighteen.

I have sometimes wondered, since then, why I
was so inefficient at acquiring the sort of knowledge which wins scholarships. It would be easy to
put the blame on the way I was taught, but my
own explanation is that I have a mind which absorbs information slowly and can only learn easily
when its visual imagination is stimulated.

Public schools haven't time to worry about the
artistic temperament or people with latent abilities
of which they themselves are unaware, and I cannot believe that I showed much promise of doing
anything out of the ordinary. If I did, nobody at
Marlborough noticed it. 'Lacks power of concen-
ration; shows no particular intelligence or aptitude
for any branch of his work; seems unlikely to
adopt any special career.' Such, as far as I remember, was my final report.

'Try to be more sensible,' was Mr. Gould's
parting advice to me when Hamo and I were in
his study saying good-bye to him. Hamo he rejected, because, without achieving anything
brilliant, he was methodical and diligent. It was
perfectly plain that whatever he set his hand to he
would do well. With me it was otherwise. 'Try to
be more sensible.' The words were offered less as a
piece of advice than as an almost absent-minded

comment on one whom he had come to regard
(with a sort of tolerant affection) as irresponsibl
and deficient in solidity of character.

Thus I departed, thinking only of cricke
matches in the holidays, and wearing an Ol
Marlburian tie, which for me was neither mor
nor less than a badge of emancipation from a
educational experience that I had found mode
ately pleasant but mentally unprofitable.

IV

While attempting to compose an outline of my own mental history, I have sometimes been interrupted by a nudging suspicion that I am not recording the past as it really was. Can it have contained so much that was intensely felt? I ask myself. Can it have been so amiably experienced, so intelligently observed? And I feel the unbending visages of the realists reproving me for failing to imitate their awful and astringent example. Let me, therefore, be on the safe side, and offer a semi-apologetic confession of my inability to describe my early life in a dismal and dissatisfied tone of voice. All human beings desire to be glad. I prefer to remember my own gladness and good luck, and to forget, whenever I can, those moods and minor events which made me low-spirited and unresponsive. Be at your best, vision enchanting, I cry. And the sun comes out on cherry orchards in full bloom; the foot-path across the fields that went to Brench-

ley and its bells goes also toward unadventured
morning-lands of heart and head, which chime and
chime again with innocent unconcern—'O world
be happy for my sake!'

Would you have me halt at the next stile, where
the path goes between the young green corn, to
doubt the existence of an all-wise Providence?
Would you have me claim that I overheard no
heavenly message in the song of the skylark, and
deny the young felicity I felt when I gazed across
the dreaming richness of the Weald? Would you
have me exchange all this for the doldrums of a
precocious disillusionment? I do not think so; and
what's more I cannot do it. Not that it would make
much difference if I did, now and then, become
glumly communicative about myself as I was when
at my adolescent worst. Turning the page, you
would sigh and hope for something better to follow. For it is humanly certain that most of us remember very little of what we have read. To open
almost any book a second time is to be reminded
that we had forgotten well-nigh everything that the
writer told us. Parting from the narrator and his narrative, we retain only a fading impression; and he
as it were, takes the book away from us and tucks
it under his arm. Thus, for the great majority, these
words will pass by, even as my figure vanishes on
that foot-path over the fields. A cloud crosses the

sun and the cherry-orchards lose their moment of entrancement. Dream-led youth has crossed the next stile and rambled on, and you, who watched him pass, will soon forget. But it was a moment of poetic discovery that I showed you, and the April morning was like youth itself—heedless and happy. Be grateful, therefore, and share my gratitude that I lived in such a pleasant region. For in those days I found no fault with the world, and did not fore-see that it would, in my lifetime, alter much.

*   *   *

From that April of 1905 I must now return to the time when I had been liberated (and superannuated) from Marlborough. I had a year to fill in before going up to Cambridge, and what was more, my Little-go examination had to be got through, which was by no means a certainty, even with assistance from the first-class cramming establishment to which I now went for three terms. I call it a cramming establishment, but it never seemed to me at all oppressively educational. In fact I felt far less crammed there than I had done at school. The tutoring was excellent and there was a leisurely uncompetitive air about one's daily routine which made study comparatively easy and unfatiguing.

From the day I went to Henley House I found
it entirely to my liking. For one thing there was no
fuss about getting there. It was less than nine
miles from my home; I merely mounted my new
bicycle and after about ten minutes on the main
road to Tunbridge Wells, took a short cut by a
lane which went through some hilly, out-of-the-
way country where I had been fondest of going for
my first real pony rides with Richardson. We always stopped on the bridge over the brook by Dun-
dale Farm, because at that point Kent ended and
Sussex began. Gazing from one county to the other,
I was never sure whether I could see any difference.
Richardson thought there wasn't, but agreed that
it was very interesting to have one foot in each
county. In the narrow lanes of that woody district
we sometimes heard the bells of a timber-wagon
and pulled up at the edge of the road to watch a
grandly straining team go past with pride of country music chiming above their manes and harness.
From far away in the little valleys of long-ago I
hear them now—those bells which rang so har-
moniously together and will never again be heard
across the oaks and orchards. Meanwhile my new
bicycle made my head feel independent of my legs,
for it had a 'free-wheel', which was a great improvement on coasting with one's feet up and the pedals
whizzing round underneath and hitting one on

he shin when one came to the bottom of a hill.

Free-wheeling along my favourite lanes on that early autumn afternoon seemed to suggest escape rom school life and nothing much to worry about luring the next twelve months. I felt a happy-go-lucky sort of person, head in air and pleasantly occupied by loosely connected ruminations, and eyes less on the ups and downs of the familiar and rather flinty road than on the woods and fields nd hop-kilns which looked so contented with the indolent September sunshine. Here was the Kentish landscape to which I was cosily accustomed; nd here was I, fully convinced that as soon as I had safely passed my Little-go I would begin in earnest the epic in twelve books of which I had lready composed the first two lines:

Sundered from earth and utterly alone,
Upon the heights of manhood stood a soul . . .

Really rather fine, that, I thought, ignoring a disrespectfully intruding notion that the soul was standing on the first tee addressing the ball which proposed to drive into eternity.

With one enormous swipe he reached the green;
Then marched toward Paradise to hole the put.

oolish thoughts like that would insist on floating into my head while I was bicycling my way through

my nineteenth year with a jumble of poetry and
Paley's *Evidences* and golf competitions in my
brain. Paley did not seem to have much connection
with the Christianity which vaguely permeated my
serious-minded moments, though he was an essential preliminary to my career at Cambridge. I did
not associate him with being confirmed either; in
fact I never even mentioned him to that broad-
minded old friend of my mother's to whose rectory I sometimes bicycled for an hour of friendly
consideration of the Catechism. But the Canon
himself was one of the most obvious evidences of
the goodness of Christianity that I had so far met
with, though he couldn't confirm me into any clear
understanding of the real meaning of religion.
Only experience can teach that. For the time being
I bicycled about with bits of Paley disporting
themselves in my head. Sometimes I invented
ridiculous variations on the original version, such
as 'Suppose the Creator to have had a Creator'
which became a refrain that I couldn't get rid of.
And after all the idea didn't sound any more prob-
lematical than lots of other things I'd been taught
to believe and had learnt so laboriously.

*   *   *

I have always been sensitive to my surroundings

nd self-adapting to people's estimation of me.
Like those insects which become the same colour
s the leaf they are sitting on, I respond readily to
arying local conditions.

At my crammer's I was considered lively and
musing, and wasn't blamed for harum-scarum
ehaviour. As a result I was consistently cheerful,
vhereas at Marlborough I had often felt moody
nd unappreciated.

The owner and director of the Henley House
stablishment (affectionately known to his past and
resent pupils as 'The Boss') allowed our high
pirits full freedom. His controlling influence was
xercised by quiet methods. The Boss was a well-
uilt, smallish man who did everything in a deli-
erate and systematic way, concealing his sense of
umour under a greying moustache and only let-
ing it twinkle occasionally from his fine dark eyes.
Ie spoke slowly, in a rich and rather deep voice, as
hough his active intelligence was somewhat sub-
ued by sense of responsibility. And responsible
e was—for the examination results of more than
wenty young men, most of whom already regarded
hemselves as mature smokers and men of the
orld, while several of them had been sent to him
n account of backwardness in their intellectual
evelopment. His steadying effect on us was, I
ink, mainly caused by his imperturbable voice

and manner. I cannot believe that the most un-
mannerly cub in creation could have been openly
rude or disrespectful to The Boss, and he must have
had a fair number of recognizably cubbish charges
during his career as a crammer.

There were occasions when our animal spirits
found an uproarious outlet. This usually took the
form of 'ragging' someone who had made himself unpopular. One evening, for instance, we had
put our victim into a narrow courtyard at the back
of the house, and were sousing him with water. No
fire-hose being available, I had collected all the
bedroom jugs I could find and the contents were
being heaved at the unfortunate youth from several
windows. This was most exhilarating and seemed
likely to go on indefinitely. I was hard at it in the
bathroom, filling jugs and passing them on to my
assistants, reserving an extra big jugful for my own
occasional use. 'Here's another!' I shouted, and
then found that I was handing a jug to The Boss.
Gravely and quite imperturbably he ignored my
offer of a jug of water to throw at young Marriot—
who had really done nothing to merit all this drench-
ing. All that The Boss said was: 'Oh, Sassoon, do
you mind using the *metal* jugs? The earthenware
ones are apt to come away from their handles.' He
then went quietly out of the bathroom, and somehow I felt that we might as well stop now. As usual

The Boss had made me realize that he understood the situation but considered that things had gone far enough.

Another delightful character at Henley House was The Boss's cousin and partner, who was known as 'Uncle' and lived in a smaller house near the disused stables. Uncle (whom I venerated as a former first-class cricketer—he had kept wicket for Kent) seemed less purposeful than The Boss. He spoke more musefully, in a slightly higher-pitched voice, and appeared to be in no hurry to reach those definite conclusions at which his cousin arrived—somewhat long-windedly but always with the end well in view. To watch Uncle dawdling along the stretch of lawn after breakfast with his pipe in his mouth, lean and rather stooping, with an odd-looking old tweed hat on the back of his head, one might have thought that he was going nowhere in particular instead of making his way to conduct army candidates through Wellington's campaigns or tread with me the well-worn path of Paley's *Evidences*. Now I come to think of it, his way of walking suggested a wicket-keeper changing ends between the overs.

'Uncle' usually seemed to be thinking about something else. Perhaps he was thinking about his hobby of golf-club making, for he had a little workshop, where in an atmosphere of pitch, glue,

and varnish, he evolved peculiarly shaped heads
for drivers and brassies with which he and several
of the pupils imported variety to their game.
'Yes, I think that shaft will suit you,' he would
say in his gentle unemphatic voice, waggling the
club outside his workshop door. Uncle's hickory
shafts, as I remember them, were sometimes stiff
as poles and sometimes so whippy that they
wriggled like eels. Anyhow he himself produced
some surprising results with them on the nine
hole course at Henley House. He was an uncertain
player. He had his record-breaking rounds, and
he had what we called his 'Rats' rounds, when he
was completely off his 'long game'. On such occasions his erratic slicings and pullings were punc-
tuated not by furious oaths but by exasperated
exclamations of 'Rats!' His 'short game' was adroit
and unconventional. He appeared to conjure rather
than hit his ball up to and into the hole. I remember an occasion when he had a fifty-foot put to
beat the record for the nine holes. The last green
was in front of the house, and all eyes were on him
as he studied the line (which hadn't been mown
for several days). After prolonged cogitation he
struck the ball with a rusty old cleek which he
favoured at the time; the ball travelled gaily over
the worm-casts, hesitated, and then plopped into
the hole. Far away in 1905 a shout goes up from

he onlookers, while Uncle with the nonchalant
ir of a man who could do it again if he'd wanted
o, saunters across to them and lights a cigarette.

*   *   *

From the present age of marvellous mechanical
ontrivances, we can, I suppose, look forward with
onfidence to the time when our own memories
ill be visually reproducible by some electrical
rocess. Authors like myself will sit in their pub-
sher's Telememoir Studio with all the most re-
ent apparatus around them; hundreds of miles of
eels of autobiography will be communicated to
ome highly sensitive medium—the actual ingre-
ients of which I am unable to predict—and the
esults will be selectionized much in the same way
s is done by our modern film industry. The radia-
on waves of authors will vary in length and inten-
ty, and there will be a few highly-paid 'writers'
ho will remember voices so sympathetically that
iey will be able to create talking Telememoirs.
ew books will be shown on the screen, and will
so be accessible—silently, of course—in enor-
ious albums. It will be a literature of scenic sen-
itions which will compete with—and possibly
ipersede—the literature of printed language.
ome of us—or rather some of them—in that

age may regret the abandonment of the old un
mechanized method of reminiscence-writing, bu
on the whole it will be regarded as an improved
and much more flexible art-form. The innovation
will, at any rate, create an unlimited supply o
authors, and no facet of human experience will be
left unrecorded. In the meantime I must continu
to transcribe my recollections in the usual way
amplifying as best I can my mental picture of tha
group on the lawn in front of Henley House.

There I see George, afterwards one of my bes
friends—known to me then as classical tutor an
all-round athlete who had played football for Cam
bridge and the Corinthians in the mid-'ninetie
and was now totting up Uncle's score, which ha
beaten his own record by a stroke. George was
man who was always glad to see someone else d
better than himself, at golf or anything else. Eve
when I first knew him his selfless character was ap
parent in his fine resolute face; remembering hi
as he was in later years I have a consistent ment:
perception of him never admitting how tired h
was, always quietly cheerful, and often radiantl
responsive to those around him. Eyes and voic
had a shining quality of courage, humour, an
intelligence. He was, in fact, one of the paragon
of my human experience—one of those men wh
go through life doing good without being awa1

of it, teaching others, by reticent example, to be more tolerant, generous, and humble. Thus for these few moments, I recover George in his anonymous glory. 'Perhaps I'm not quite such a sound chap as you seem to think,' he remarks, turning away with his self-restricting smile, just as he is doing in the living and natural photograph I am looking at now, where he is spraying the sand in a tee-box with a watering-can.

While writing about my youth I have tried to feel young again; I have even made efforts to feel childish, when childhood was my theme. But when describing my approaches to manhood I have sometimes been prematurely aged by sensations reserved for those of riper years. To put it plainly, my rememberings of educational experience have made me wish that I could credit the growing boy with some sympathy for his instructors. It is, of course, useless to expect the young to realize what it feels like to be tired in a time-worn way. Nevertheless I have found myself wanting to be back there so that I could, just for once, communicate my fellow-feeling to some of those people whose grey hairs I took for granted—and perhaps made slightly greyer. There was The Boss, for instance; actively energetic and well under fifty, but never getting much relief from duties and anxieties. When he was sitting in his own room doing his

accounts, someone would surely burst in and con
sult him about something. Seeking refreshment i
the financial columns of *The Times*, escaping per
haps into an imaginary speculation in Rand Mine
or Rubber, he would surely have preferred to b
unaware that a game of indoor hockey was goin
on in the large carpetless room where most of hi
pupils acquired knowledge by day and disporte
themselves of an evening. It mattered nothing t
them if a window was broken or a gas-glob
smashed. Many of them belonged to wealth
families, and had I been The Boss (and also thirt
years older than I was then) I would have blame
that Christian Creator, whom Paley had suppose
to be so evident, for not having permitted me t
handle their investments instead of their educa
tion. But I am sure he never did that, though h
may have wished that he was farming some of the
parental acres, agriculture being an occupation to
ward which he was favourably inclined. Mean
while he puffed his pipe philosophically, sitting i
his wicker chair, wearing his old dark-green colleg
blazer and wondering whether Rio Tintos, whic
were up a couple of points, would drop again ne
day, while his daughter Jane cleaned her golf clu
and wondered why she couldn't enjoy Mrs. Me
nell's *Poems* which had been so strongly recon
mended by her late schoolmistress.

Among my contemporaries at Henley House I had found a friend who comes in appropriately at this point, because he was, in the best sense of the words, older than his age. Tommy hailed from Cumberland and had a certain north-country shrewdness about him. He was small, red-haired, and alert, with eyes which often had a look of being puckered up to encounter wintry weather. He had very nice manners, which could take the form of behaving with sympathetic understanding of his elders. He had a delightfully cronyish quality, and when I took him over to see my mother they became like one mind in their mutual interest in growing roses from the dissimilar soils of Cumberland and Kent. With me he shared enthusiasm for golf, and we had already resolved that when we were proficient and full of money we would make a tour of the championship courses of Great Britain, ending up at St. Andrews.

For the present, however, our objectives were the rival universities, and Tommy, whose education had been interfered with by ill health, was having an uphill struggle to reach Oxford via Virgil and Homer. George was his instructor and hero, but he kept a warm corner in his heart for The Boss, and I have a clear mental picture of them conversing at the end of a meal when everyone else had left the table (except, it would seem, myself).

Tommy, a modest and excellent listener, was always willing to absorb The Boss's monologues about the pros and cons of chemical manures or the relative merits of mortgages and debentures. I used to assert that on one occasion The Boss concluded a lengthy financial discourse with 'So the end of it was, Tommy, that the mortgagees foreclosed and the debenture-holders went into liquidation'—a joke which I made threadbare by repetition.

I have spoken of my desire not to remember unpleasant things very clearly. My intention in this book has been to commemorate or memorialize those human contacts which supported me in my rather simple-minded belief that the world was full of extremely nice people if only one could get to know them properly. So I hope to be forgiven for mentioning yet another likeable character, who happened to be the type of man who wouldn't expect to be mentioned at all. 'The Teacher', as he was called, constituted the fourth member of the Henley House staff, and was a person who seldom drew attention to himself. He just taught—quietly, persistently, and admirably. I don't know whether he thought of himself as 'Teacher', but everyone else did, and if he had been addressed by his real name he would probably have decided that he was being made fun of. He taught me French, in a little

room of his own, where I steadily construed my
way through the set subjects for the Little-go. In
his calm and literal way The Teacher took me
through that well-known farcical comedy *Le Voyage
de Monsieur Perrichon*. Neither of us wasted time
in finding it funny. There was also *The Cid Ballads*
by Victor Hugo, whom I knew by name as author
of *Les Misérables*, which I felt no inclination to
read. I found The Cid a great bore, but liked him
because he was easy to translate. What The Teacher
thought about him was never divulged, for he kept
his opinions to himself, except when consulted. His
countenance suggested that he might have been a
clergyman; I could imagine him being one, in surroundings of Wordsworthian simplicity. In fact he
somehow reminded me of Wordsworth, though I
can't quite say why. He always wore a high single
collar, even when he played his steady rounds of
golf, or when, in the summer, he bicycled slowly
about the country by himself. And from behind
that high collar I see him now, looking at me in his
mildly quizzical way, and wondering perhaps, like
old Mr. Gould, whether I shall ever learn to be
more sensible. Far too modest to be capable of
venturing an opinion about the future, he gets
up to open the window. It is the first week in
March and warm for the time of year—thirty-
three years ago. After listening for a few moments

he returns to his chair. 'That's the first time I've heard a blackbird sing this year,' he remarks, and we continue with The Cid. It was spring for me, and poetry was awakening my senses to ignorant rapture. For him, it seemed, there was only a gentle acquiescence in the transition from one season of examinations to another. The Teacher was there to help youth to pass the preliminary examination which led to life. He had no great things to hope for; next year, perhaps, he would buy a new bicycle. Frugal and unenvious, he watched us go our ways, little knowing that one at least would return to him long afterwards with commemorative affection.

V

There is no need to be exact about the date, but is somewhere in the early part of June 1906, and bout five o'clock in the morning. In broad day-ght, under a quietly overclouded sky, a dozen oung people are arranging themselves before the anopied fountain in the market-place at Cam-ridge. They have danced to the end of the Trinity oat Club Ball and are about to corroborate the ccasion by being photographed.

They are doing it in a good-natured unresisting rt of way, for it is a family party and they all ke one another's presence as a matter of course, ithout any nonsense about wondering when they ill meet again.

My cousin Alyce stifles a yawn and feels sure at the camera will catch her in the middle of the ext one; my cousin Joan tells her brother Oliver put his tie straight; the photographer emerges om black velvet obscurity, regards the group

with a stabilizing simper, and removes the cap
for three seconds time holds its breath, and then
relaxes us into animation again. A clock strikes
five and the young people disappear in various
directions, unaware that I shall have my eye on
them more than thirty years afterwards. Scrutinizing that faded photograph now, I see myself surrounded by my cousins—the girls looking absent-
mindedly amused and the men rather stolid and
serious. There is that modest hero Malcolm, a
stalwart Rowing Blue, destined to become an
eminent surgeon. And his younger brother, who
went into the Indian Army. And Oliver, who was
to do well as an engineer. And my brother Hamo
whose engineering ambitions were sacrificed on
the Gallipoli peninsula. And there am I, sitting on
the ground in front, with a serenely vacant countenance which suggests that no plans for a practical career have as yet entered my head. Behind
that head the jet of the drinking-fountain is just
visible, as though the camera were hinting that my
name would be written in water, which was what
myself sometimes foresaw.

It had been a jolly fine dance anyhow, I thought,
picking up my cap and gown and taking my tired
patent-leather feet across to my rooms, which were
only about fifty yards from the fountain. And after
all I wasn't quite nobody, for I'd got a whole

column of blank verse (semi-facetious, in the manner of Browning) in the May Week Number of *The Granta*; it was a monologue by an anarchist who blew himself up when about to drop his bomb from a window on to a royal procession, and I had no notion why I had written it, except that I had wanted to follow up my exultant parody of Stephen Phillips, which had appeared in the previous week and had been about lovers alliteratively involved in a motor accident. And now I was back in my low-ceilinged room on the third floor, with *The Granta* lying on the writing-table, and *Atalanta in Calydon* open beside it, and the inappropriate daylight making it all look somehow as though time were playing a trick on me and I were seeing something which had happened before. The room looked too quiet to be quite real, and the reproductions of Rossetti and Burne-Jones were raptly remote from the dizzy waltzing I'd done in the Guildhall. Standing there for a moment, it was like changing from one of my selves to another. For a few hours I had been escaping from my everyday self, and here he was waiting up for me, telling me to get rid of my buttonhole and evening clothes, stop writing silly parodies, and do some real drudgery for those examinations which I didn't seem to have a ghost of a chance of getting through.

Perhaps for the first time, I had the sense of

time slipping away from me, of not making serious
use of my opportunities; and mixed up with this
was the reiterated memory of a waltz tune which
meant nothing but an allurement to forgetfulness
and the pursuit of easy poetic emotion and idle
pleasure. 'In three months I shall be twenty, and
I don't seem to have done anything at Cambridge
except buy books in vellum bindings,' I thought
while the clock watched me with its hands at half-
past five and I overheard my thought as though it
were a repetition of some previous experience.

*   *   *

It really seemed that in order to make a success
of being up at Cambridge I needed to be three
people at once. There was the swing-concerned
person who so frequently spent his afternoon golf-
ing at Mildenhall or Royston. There was he who
sat up into the small hours composing high-
principled poetry about nothing in particular.
And—heaven help him—there was the one who
ought to have been—and wasn't—advancing toward the acquisition of a University Degree. There
was even a fluid fourth, who sprawled about in
other people's rooms talking irrepressible nonsense
or listening to someone playing Chopin scherzos
on the pianola. The only thing these four had

ommon was that they neither smoked nor im-
ibed alcohol, and received £80 a term through
heir family solicitor.

They—or rather I—having come to the end of
iy first year, the College Tutor was only partly
ware that my academic future was precarious. He
ad assumed from the start that I was fully capable
f passing Tripos examinations, and for a time I
ad allowed myself to be influenced by his urgent
ptimism. My guardians were of opinion that after
left Cambridge the wisest thing for me to do
ould be to read for the Bar, and it was suggested
at this would somehow coincide with my lean-
gs toward literature. Since working for an or-
nary degree would have meant more mathematics,
decided that anything would be better than that,
d plunged blindly into the Law Tripos. Grap-
ing with the *Edicts of Gaius and Justinian*, I
emorized much information about the manu-
ission of slaves, and other, to me, meaningless
cient Roman legal procedure. Dutifully I at-
nded droning lectures, desperately scribbling
gments of what I overheard and seldom under-
inding what my notes were about when I perused
em in private. Note-taking seemed to be physical
ther than mental exercise. During my first term
submitted to my doom without realizing that
thing but a miracle could enable me to propi-

tiate the examiners. The Lent term reduced me to
blank despondency. Toiling at my text-books, I
discovered again and again that I had turned over
two pages at once without noticing anything wrong.
In the eyes of my Law Coach, whom I attended
twice a week, I became a manifest absurdity. He
was a dark and dapper little LL.D. who had written a book about the Hague Conference and wore
a rich-red tie and a neatly waxed moustache. In
after-years he became an important authority in
the world of International Law. Precise and persistent, he took about half a dozen pupils at a time.
The subjects he was teaching afforded him scant
opportunities for humour, but on one occasion he
caused a mild explosion of mirth—at my expense
—by exclaiming: 'If I were to go out into the
street and interrogate the first errand-boy I met
he couldn't know less than you do about Maine's
International Law!'

This, I think, was the irrefutable remark which
finally impelled me to call on the senior tutor of
my college and announce my inability to learn any
more Law. In my agitation I put it to him quite
unashamedly that I was more interested in poetry
than anything else. To my surprise and relief he
responded sympathetically. For a few minutes he
almost forgot that he was a senior tutor and revealed
a warm admiration for Browning. I had entered his

rooms in College a palpitating and self-ploughed candidate for my Tripos, and here we were, amicably enthusing over the glories of 'Abt Vogler' and 'Saul'. I could have embraced him when he declared that Law certainly allowed no scope at all for poetic imagination, and his proposal that I should transfer my attentions to the History Tripos was almost like receiving an honorary degree. So elated was I as I went out that I tripped and fell down the first flight of drumming wooden stairs, and landed with such a bump that the little man popped his head round the door to see what had happened.

'Dear me, what an impetuous fellow you are!' he exclaimed, as I arose, rubbing a bruised funny-bone. The senior tutor was a fussy, over-anxious man with a nervous stammer, which I used to catch when conversing with him. When we were together it was difficult to decide which was the jumpier and more jerky of the two. Continually twiddling his eyeglasses, he specialized in sudden darting movements which sometimes knocked things off tables, while I relied mainly on fidgeting with my fingers and feet. In fact, though favourably disposed toward one another, we were not unlike a couple of cats on hot bricks, and my exit from our crucial conference was quite characteristic. After this flying start I tackled the History

Tripos with a spurt of unmethodical energy. I had
found Law altogether too inhuman and arid, bu
History was bound to be much more lively and
picturesque, and I got to work on the reign o
Louis XI without any feeling of repugnance. The
memoirs of Philip de Commines, in a seventeenth
century translation, made quite enjoyable reading
with their quaint literary flavour. But I soon dis
covered that I didn't retain much of them after
wards. I could only remember episodes which
appealed to my visual imagination, such as the aneo
dote of Louis XI's scouts mistaking tall thistles fo
the spears of men-at-arms. Chastellain's memoir
which I also had to read, brought me to a stand
still, for they were in medieval French and n
translation was available. The more I looked a
Chastellain the less hopeful I felt of being able t
get past him. He was incomprehensible, bulky
and ominously bound in black buckram. My mai
trouble as a student of history was that I wante
it to be more like Stanley Weyman's novels c
Shakespeare's plays. I had but a feeble grasp c
constructive elements and political interworking

In fact it never consciously occurred to me th
a prime minister in a richly furred robe was muc
the same as one who wore a frock-coat. I coul
only understand what history signified when it w
being either dramatic or chronological. Dodgin

about in Thatcher and Schwill's *General History of Europe* I found little, except dates and names, which I could reproduce verbally to my history coach; he complained of my preoccupation with the career of Joan of Arc, about whom I was privately meditating a long poem in blank verse. 'You really must put in some solid work on the struggle between the Empire and the Papacy,' he remarked. To which I dutifully agreed, and spent most of the next day reading *The Earthly Paradise* in a punt. By reading I mean that my eyes moved from line to line while I overheard rather than 'took in' the beautifully monotonous word music of William Morris, which loitered through my mind as though it were one with the riverside sounds of that golden day in early summer. At that time I was finding much material for day-dreaming in the poems and pictures of the Praeraphaelite Brotherhood. Through them I shared an imaginative existence which, as they had intended it to do, provided an ideal escape from commonplace actualities. As ordinary human beings I didn't want to know too much about them, and had been rather sorry when my mother told me that Rossetti took chloral and suffered from insomnia, and that Morris had become an ardent Socialist in his later years. I preferred to think vaguely of them as a group of people with whom I could have been

happy, and I wanted their world to resemble the
one which they had created for me in their works.
I imagined myself conversing with them to the
music of citterns and citoles (though uncertain
what those obsolete instruments would sound like),
in arrassed rooms whose windows overlooked a
river that flowed down to Camelot. Far away from
factory chimneys, Rossetti would be reading me
his latest sonnet, or Morris showing me the carp
in his fish-pond, and my own poems would be
being exquisitely printed by the Kelmscott Press
and bound in limp vellum with woven silk ties.
Actually I had never met anyone, except myself,
who wanted to be a poet, so I often sought com-
panionship in the past, pretending that I had been
at Cambridge with Tennyson, and having long
talks with him and Edward Fitzgerald. At any moment they might come along the river-bank and
get into my punt. Or else it would be Morris, arm-
in-arm with Rossetti and the late Sir Edward Burne-
Jones. As an offset to all this make-believe, I could
claim that I had once met Mrs. William Morris
who had been brought to see my mother when I
was about six years old. I could remember a stately
lady entering our nursery; but being shy, I refused
to emerge from under the table, so I only viewed
the original of Rossetti's picture, 'The Blessed
Damozel', through the fringe of the table-cloth.

Anyhow here I was, under a pollard willow, with a light breeze ruffling the bend of the river and bringing the scent of bean-fields, while Cambridge, a mile or two away, dozed in its academic afternoon. Successfully though I had interposed *The Earthly Paradise* between myself and the struggle of the Empire and the Papacy, I couldn't evade the fact that I was due for the first part of my History Tripos in twelve months' time. And what would happen then, I asked myself, removing my eyes from the lulling stanzas of *Pygmalion and the Image*. Nothing, I was certain, could possibly happen except an unqualified exposure of my ignorance and incompetence. I was well on my way to a fiasco of the first water, I thought, wondering whether a fiasco could also be of the deepest dye. The fact that I had been pouring out poems which seemed to me quite good made no difference to the fact that I should be chucked out of Cambridge at the end of my second year.

*   *   *

Toward the end of that summer term my Uncle Hamo came to Cambridge and I gave him an overwhelming luncheon of lobster mayonnaise, the best college hock, and everything festive I could think of. If I could have the ordering of that meal

again I would give him some good Cheshire cheese
a nice brown loaf, and a tankard of home-brewe(
ale, and possibly a cold gooseberry tart. Simpl
country things were what he liked best, and h
always had the look of an open-air man, as well h
might, since he came of a line of thriving gentleme)
farmers in Cheshire. Had anyone remarked to m
at that time, 'What a modest man Mr. Thornycrof
is,' I should probably have replied, 'Yes, I suppos
you're right.' Years afterwards, when someon
rather effusively informed me that my Uncle Ham(
was the most unassuming distinguished man he'(
ever met, I no longer needed to have this brough
to my notice. In 1906, however, his modesty ha(
not struck me as anything remarkable. It seem
odd that I shouldn't, even then, have admired hi
self-effacing simplicity, instead of taking him fo
granted as a greatly gifted person who had becom
an eminent sculptor on his merits. I was proud o
him, of course, and very anxious to win his goo(
opinion; but I had never seen much of him, an(
couldn't confide in him how depressed I was feel
ing about my university work. 'You should tr
for the Chancellor's Medal, old man,' he sug
gested in his quiet way, when I had diffidentl
informed him that I'd been writing a goo(
deal of poetry lately. This idea hadn't occurre(
to me before, but it now seemed to be my onl

chance of earning academic distinction. Tennyson,
I knew, had won the medal with a poem about
Timbuctoo, and it comforted me to remember that
he had also left Cambridge without taking a degree.
Uncle Hamo himself had won three Royal Academy medals before he was twenty-two, which
might be taken as a favourable omen for me. But
he wasn't a poet and hadn't been compelled to
combine sculpture with stuffing his brain full of
irrelevant knowledge for university examinations.
There were times when I wished that I were a
sculptor myself—like Pygmalion in *The Earthly
Paradise* when

'. . . as the white chips from the chisel flew
Of other matters languidly he dreamed,
For easy to his hand that labour seemed.'

Anyhow if I could secure the medal it would do
something to counteract the certain disaster which
awaited me in the History Tripos. Yes, I thought,
finishing off the hock after Uncle Hamo's departure (though I couldn't so far get much enjoyment
out of drinking wine), I would write a magnificent
poem, win the prize, and create a tremendous sensation when I declaimed it in the Senate House
next spring. You would be able to hear a pin drop
when I reached my peroration, and the whole
audience would rise to its feet and cheer me when

the concluding line had either trumpeted or whispered—I wasn't yet sure which it would be—from my lips. 'Exquisitely mourned in sorrows mute'—a line I had thought of lately—must be worked in somehow; and perhaps a few lessons in elocution would be advisable.

I had to wait till October before the subject of next year's poem was announced. It turned out to be 'Edward the First', which was very propitious, for Uncle Hamo had made an equestrian statue of that monarch and I had always admired it greatly. I was now confronted by the problem of how to compose the poem itself. Something statuesque seemed most suitable, though I was drawn toward dramatic monologue and dashed off a rough Browningesque beginning, in which the King was thinking things over on the eve of the Battle of Crecy. Next day I bought Professor Tout's monograph and was somewhat taken aback by discovering that Crecy was fought about forty years after Edward the First died. Tout had rather a chilling effect on my imagination, and the *Dictionary of National Biography* (which I consulted in the Union Library) made things no better. Edward's career seemed to have consisted entirely in legislative activity, military adventure, quelling baronial rebellions, confirming charters, stag-hunting and hawking. He didn't appear to have had any emo-

tional experiences worth mentioning. I found by
experiment that mere paraphrasing of dry historical details could only produce such flat results
as:

> His presence was required in Gascony
> Though the immediate cause of his departure
> Was t' act as mediator in the long
> Quarrel between the French and Aragonese
> For the possession of Sicily.

I decided that it would be necessary to say something about his having been the founder of our
parliamentary system. But how could one wrap it
up in more memorable words?

> Conservatives and Liberals alike
> From him first sprang, and carry on his work.

It was obvious that I should never win the medal
by showing up stuff like that. An attempt at clear
thinking resulted in my making the following
note: 'Poem must be strictly accurate historically;
Plantagenet in general outlook; work in E.'s high
ideals wherever possible; way of doing it needs
deciding on.' 'Way of doing it' meant what poet
should I, more or less, allow myself to be influenced
by. I was already discovering that I had an aptitude for imitating various verse styles, and now felt
that my poem ought not to be too Praeraphaelitish

277

in treatment if I were to adhere strictly to the general outlook of the Plantagenets. I therefore made a further note: 'Why not soliloquy by E. as young man on Crusade (after capturing Nazareth?) remembering past pleasures at home, and then having vision of future efforts to improve condition of Christianity in English realm while on throne.' But there again one was in danger of losing touch with historical accuracy; dramatic monologues so easily lapsed into one's own personal opinions. So in the end I decided on a straightforward retrospect dictated by the King to an anonymous chronicler toward the close of his reign. The King, I felt, must keep himself out of it as much as he could, and stick to important national events.

But when, exiled from afflatus, I had compiled about half the allotted two hundred lines, I dried up in despair. Instead of seeming to be Edward the First, it was obviously only Professor Tout talking in very prosy blank verse. Also it was evident that it would take me two thousand lines at least to cover the ground of Edward's activities. Among other things he'd had six sons and ten daughters, though several of them had died quite young.

It was now the end of October, and I felt that I might just as well try to write seductively about Euclid as about Edward I. A fortnight ago I had looked on him as a noble and likeable figure, but his achievements now seemed a mere catalogue of medieval maraudings and obnoxious statute-makings and I had lost all sympathy for any private feelings that he might have had.

So I removed from my writing-table the photograph of Uncle Hamo's beautiful statue of him as a young man on a mettlesome horse, and gave up hope that I should ever produce anything appropriate, though the date for sending in was still more than two months ahead. Meanwhile I was consoled by having my first volume of poems in active preparation; it was, in fact, actually 'in the press', and had been there more than a month. No one knew about it, not even my mother, for whom it was to be a splendid surprise. When I say 'no one', I mean no one except me and The Athenæum Press.

It was on my twentieth birthday that I had definitely resolved to seek a printer. My ideas of how to set about it were hazy and my attitude to printers was humble-minded and tentative. I assumed that it would cost more than I could afford to print fifty copies—probably quite thirty pounds —but felt almost grateful to The Athenæum Press when they agreed to do it for me, no price being mentioned. I was a regular and respectful reader of *The Athenæum*. Unaware that it was no longer the most influential literary paper in England, I assumed that to be cordially reviewed by it was not unlike being elected a member of The Athenæum club because one was distinguished, as both my Thornycroft uncles had been. Printed by J. E. Francis & Co., I observed. So I wrote them a modest but business-like letter, inquiring whether they would consider printing my poems for me. When, instead of declining with dignity owing to pressure of more important work, they replied that they would, I felt that I had gained admittance to the literary world and gladly placed my manuscript in their hands without asking for further details.

The name Francis seemed suitable, for my great-grandfather had been John Francis, a well-known sculptor. Had I been better informed I should also have known that before I was born another John Francis had published the omnisciently authoritative *Athenæum* for more than fifty years and had been highly esteemed as the editor of *Notes and Queries*. So my uncalculative selection of a printer could scarcely have been more felicitous.

In an old note-book I find a brief entry recording that I sent off the manuscript on September 20th, received the first proofs a fortnight later, added some lines called 'Aspiration', and had returned the second set of proofs early in Novem-

ber. After that there was nothing to be done except
await my fifty copies and decide about the people
to whom I should send them. But the Athenæum Press did things in an unhastening way;
by the beginning of December I became impatient and wrote a polite letter asking whether
my volume would be ready before Christmas as I
wished to circulate copies by then. They replied
that they had been awaiting my final instructions.
This relieved my anxiety, and on December 18th
the edition arrived, with a bill for seven pounds,
which seemed surprisingly little for them to charge.

The book numbered thirty-six pages and was
bound in thick white cartridge paper. The title-
page was printed on the cover as well as inside, and
the whole was held together by a narrow dark-
blue satin ribbon. My book was anonymous. On
the title-page I had put four lines by Swinburne,
which expressed an exuberant belief in my poetic
vocation. (They were from the Dedication to his
drama *Marino Faliero*.)

'Our words and works, our thoughts and songs,
    turn thither,
Toward one great end, as waves that press and roll.
Though waves be spent and ebb like hopes that
    wither,
These shall subside not ere they find the goal.'

The paper, however, was poor, and has since shown a tendency to break out into small yellow spots like iron-mould. But there were two extra copies on hand-made paper, and about twenty-five years afterwards one of these was sold for three times the original price of the whole edition—rarity, rather than literary merit, being the cause of this remarkable rise in value.

Since the end of the university term I had become involved in a second burst of creative activity about Edward the First. Some compensating mental reflex (as it would now be called) had enabled me to approach him from a more congenial point of view. Putting Professor Tout almost entirely out of mind, I relaxed into a spiritual and ideal transmutation of my subject-matter. The King was now about to pass away and had turned his back on temporal affairs. All his inherent nobility of nature was finding solemn expression in blank verse which almost made me feel as if I were bidding farewell to the world myself. As far as I can remember he was recognizably related to Tennyson's King Arthur, serene and saintly, and aloof from the concerns of statesmanship and his paternity of our modern parliamentary system. He had, in fact, forgotten all that he had ever learned and was well on his way to a better world. Having completed the poem by Christmas I came to the conclusion that it was very impressive and almost certain to win me the medal. My mother was equally hopeful. She could see that I had put plenty of genuine poetic feeling into it, and assumed that this would be worth more to me than conventional versifying combined with historical erudition.

The result would be announced in February, and in the meantime my Tripos work weighed heavily on my mind. I was making no headway at all with Stubbs's *Constitutional History and Select Charters*. It seemed that I might just as well have been learning Bradshaw's Railway Guide, which would have been much easier to memorize and would anyhow have given me a feeling that I was getting somewhere. As a contrast to Stubbs I was reading the *Life of Kate Greenaway*, with copious coloured illustrations, and I could surely have chosen no pleasanter antidote. When the term began, an attack of influenza prevented me from returning. After I had fully recovered, an inward voice suggested that I should remain at home until the result of the Chancellor's Medal had reached me. I did.

Somebody else, of course, had been awarded it, and my disappointment was acute. My mother tried to make the best of things by calling it the Chancellor's Muddle and then said no more about it.

As far as I was concerned, the verdict settled the question of returning to Cambridge there and then. Let the college tutor and my guardians say what they liked—nothing would induce me to read another word of Stubbs. Henceforth I would be a poet pure and simple. I had never really wanted to be a B.A. and now I was free from all obligation to try for it. My mother agreed with me. She thought that I should be wasting my time by trying to learn things which didn't interest me, and should do better by educating myself in the art of poetry, which was obviously the only thing for which I had a natural gift.

*   *   *

I had acquired quite a collection of encouraging letters about my printed poems. None of my readers considered themselves qualified to be critical or if they did, they concealed it, so I was spared the shock of being warned that my ideas lacked originality and that most of them were expressed in hopelessly hackneyed language. The word cliché was as yet unknown to me, and I neither knew nor cared whether I was writing platitudes or not.

'Doubt not the light of Heaven upon the soul,' I exclaimed in the very first line on page one of

ny book, and went on to say, in the next stanza:
Doubt not the rapture of the smitten lyre.' And the
nore I smote the more poetical I felt, and the less
doubted the less I bothered whether anyone else
ad referred to death as 'the merciful Healer of
voes', or youth as 'vernal ecstasy'. Nor did I ask
nyself whether my lofty adjurations about life and
uman conduct had any bearing on the situation
vith regard to my leaving college after four terms.

Is it well to play the idler in life?—to dream by
    the marge,
'earing the current of action that haply tends
    toward the best.'

That had been my question; but it merely led to
lyrical assertion of my preference for the marge
s compared with what I called 'the house of toil'.
    Meanwhile the news of my exodus from Cam-
ridge had to be broken to my guardians. My policy
vas to begin by lying low and letting it leak out
radually. This phase was soon over. The news
eached Uncle Hamo through my college tutor,
nd he wrote me an urgent letter of exhortation
nd advice, all of which I should have actively
greed with had I possessed the faintest hope of
assing my Tripos examinations.
    It was quite true about my refusal to apply my
alents to work which wasn't altogether congenial

to me and the need to show what I was worth an
prove to myself that I was capable of overcomin
difficulties. It pained me deeply that my uncl
should be so disappointed in me and should seer
to regard me as indolent and a predestined failur
in life. But how could he know what sort c
a brain I'd got? All my subsequent experience ha
shown that I have a brain which is only active i
episodic bursts of energy. Unmethodical throug
lack of training and by temperament, I had alway
been a slow and groping learner, and when cor
fronted by a mass of text-book information I be
came helpless and unintelligent, and my brai
rebelled against being loaded up with knowledg
which I felt could be of no possible use to it. If
couldn't be an imaginative writer, I thought,
would rather be a ploughman—or at any rat
watch other people ploughing, and write poem
about it. So I replied, rather petulantly, that
people liked to think me a hopeless slacker
couldn't help it; I wasn't going to swot up an
more of Stubbs's mouldy old charters to pleas
anyone. 'You say that my admission of defeat wi
cause me to lose caste with my contemporaries,'
wrote. 'This makes no difference to me because s
far I don't seem to have discovered any contem
poraries to lose caste with.'

Having thus offended Uncle Hamo and waste

some of his valuable time, I relapsed into enjoyment of my intellectual freedom. I was planning
a longish dramatic poem which was to be about
either Orpheus or Apollo—I hadn't yet made up
my mind which.

VI

My twenty-first birthday was a notably unobtrusive one. In any case I should have preferred no fuss to be made about it, and there seemed very little reason why I should invite anyone to come and pat me on the back because I'd got five or six hundred a year and no future except the possibility of becoming a poet. Both my brothers were away from home at the time; and as my mother was still recovering from a breakdown of her health we were glad to be able to spend the day (which happened to be a Sunday) in affectionate tranquillity. She knew that for me a quiet day wasn't necessarily a dull one; and the idea of not having my health drunk at a large dinner-party where I should have been expected to make a speech caused me sober satisfaction.

Coming of age merely meant that I woke up and looked out of the window and observed a heavy dew on the grass, and a green woodpecker stumping about on the tennis lawn among break-fasting blackbirds and thrushes. It was evidently going to be another gloriously fine day. The air smelt faintly of autumn; there was a white mist along the valley; and the horizon seemed, as usual, to be suggesting that I should start out on my travels and see for myself what I had hitherto only read about or imagined. But the trouble about going abroad was that I didn't know how to do it. My mother, who hadn't been out of England for the last twenty years, talked vaguely of the dis-comforts of travelling in Italy, and I didn't appear to have any ability for picking up languages, and altogether it seemed that I was fonder of the Kentish horizon than I was of the places beyond it.

It seems to me now that my youthful person-ality had no shape or coherence unless I was inside the radius of my limited experience. Looking out of the window and wondering whether it was a good omen that my birthday was on a Sunday—and a cloudless one into the bargain—I was, so to speak, on my own ground. But if that immature person were to turn round and begin airing his impulsive opinions on life and literature we should very soon have heard enough. It would be much the same as being obliged to listen while he tried to play Chopin and Grieg on the grand piano which he had rather imprudently acquired and would pay for by tedious instalments.

*   *   *

Out in the Studio in the middle of the morning, it seemed that nothing surprising could possibly happen. In the big upstairs room, which now contained my collection of books, I had resolved to do a couple of hours steady reading. First of all, however, I had to make up my mind where to hang the large photograph of *The Days of Creation* by Burne-Jones which my mother had given me. After that I decided that I really must read some Ruskin, in whom I had heavy arrears to make up, for during my final term at Cambridge I had somewhat fortuitously subscribed for that Library Edition of his works which was being gradually issued in thirty-nine volumes. Thirty of them had already arrived, and they were uniformly corpulent. So far, I had looked only at the illustrations, which were almost equivalent to foreign travel. Attracted by its name, I made a start with *The Crown of Wild Olive*; but after a few pages I lost the thread and lapsed into leaf-cutting—an occupation which was more compatible with my wandering thoughts. I might have continued cutting the leaves of Ruskin's works for the rest of the morning; but I began to be bothered by the flutterings of a butterfly imprisoned between the skylight and the gauze that was tacked over it to soften the glare.

By standing on a chair—which I placed on a table—I could just get my hand between the gauze and the glass. The butterfly was ungratefully elusive, and more than once the chair almost toppled over. Successful at last, I climbed down, and was about to put the butterfly out of the window when I observed between my fingers that it wasn't the Small Tortoiseshell or Cabbage White that I had assumed it to be. Its dark wings had yellowish borders with blue spots on them. It was more than seven years since I had entomologically squeezed the thorax of a 'specimen'. Doing so now, I discovered that one of the loftiest ambitions of my childhood had been belatedly realized. I had caught a Camberwell Beauty.

Had this occurred in my collecting days, what ecstasy I should have experienced! Even to have seen such a rarity and failed to catch it would have been the most memorable event in my career. Camberwell Beauties were reputed to be almost extinct in England, and this one was probably an immigrant. It certainly looked as though it had been knocking about the world a good deal while on its way to the Studio; but there it was—casually

caught, and now ironically reminding me that i
was no longer the apex of my ambitions.

Rather strange that it should have arrived on
this particular day, I thought, hoping it was an
augury that my more mature dreams of success
would come true, and disregarding the inference
that they too might materialize belatedly.

Placing my defunct but distinguished visitor on
the window-ledge, I stared out at the Weald and
wondered where he—for it appeared to be a male
—had come from, and how long it was since the
last one had been captured in Kent. Happy enough
the outside world looked, on that perfect September morning. And pleasant enough was the intimate world of my large airy room, with its newly
painted peacock-blue walls and the almost impres-
sive-looking array of books in old leather and
vellum bindings. If surroundings make any difference I ought to be able to do some good writing
up here, I thought, wondering what the room had
looked like when my father used it, in the year
before I was born and before I could remember
anything. From this window where I now stood
he had done a panoramic and amateurish water
colour of the view across the Weald; very green
and uninhabited he had made it look, though perhaps he had left out some of the distant details on
purpose. My mother would have made it look

much more what it really was in those years which
were now like the first few pages of a story. How
difficult it is to measure time by distance! My
father had only been dead twelve years, but it now
seemed much longer ago than that.

I had noticed that for elderly people the past
wasn't nearly so far away as it was for me. The
one-legged shoemaker who umpired in our village
matches sometimes talked about my father. 'A rare
good one he was at getting his bat down to a
shooter,' he would remark, evidently thinking of
the shooter as something quite recent, though it
must have been fully twenty years since my father
had played cricket on Matfield Green.

The Studio itself was only two years older than
I was, but I thought of it as having had quite a
long life already. And there again, how confusing
time was! For my own existence felt as if it had
been a comparatively short one, even allowing for
the fact that I couldn't clearly remember more
than fifteen years of it. My own recollections
wouldn't make much of a book, I thought; but
if only the Studio could write reminiscences of its
grown-up childhood how interesting they would
be! My mother seldom spoke of those times, but
the Studio had seen the happiness that came before those sad events which had so impressed
themselves on my mind; and I would have liked

to hear more about my father as he was at his best.

The Studio must often have heard him playing his Stradivarius with that gipsy wildness which was the special quality of his fiddling; for he was a brilliant player and had studied with Sarasate. It had heard light-hearted laughter too, and voices talking of the future without foreboding. The past had filled the Studio with vibrations that were one with my own history; but I had no wizardry to evoke them. Far, far away was my mother's youthful face as she finished her picture of the Nativity or that splendid one called *The Hours* which had been so much admired at the Royal Academy while I was still learning to walk.

For a moment I felt as if my father were in the room. So real had my meditations made him that I could almost smell his cigar smoke. And it occurred to me, for the first time, that had he lived on till now everything would have been different. Probably I shouldn't be here at all, I thought, with a new and dizzy awareness of the accidentalness of one's life, and how what appear so pre-arranged and unalterable is really the result of a series of casual happenings. But my father was such an incalculable character that it was useless to try to imagine what effect he would have had on my upbringing. At any rate I should have had another set of memories mixed up with the ones I'd already got, and life would have been a much more complicated affair altogether.

Perhaps the Camberwell Beauty had flown across the Channel to remind me of the foreign countries to which my father had always said he would take me. Perhaps it *was* my father. Anyhow the idea of his spirit assuming the form of a somewhat battered specimen of *Vanessa Antiopa* and being solemnly 'set' by me would have struck him as funny.

And again it seemed that I was not alone with my thoughts, and that some presence came between me and the buzzing tranquillity of the garden and the quiet sunlit room. But it was only the imagination of a moment; and when I turned away from the window everything looked stolid and immune from mystery. Ruskin was dead, but his *Collected Works* lived on, in a very nice red buckram binding. I was young; and what had death to do with me? To be dead was unbelievable, or at any rate as difficult to realize as last winter's snowfall. There was only the dazzling daydream of visible existence, and the serenity of poems and pictures, and past and future meeting in a siesta of weather which was neither summer nor autumn.

*   *   *

I had heard my mother moving about in the lower studio, but when I carried the Camberwell Beauty down to show her she had disappeared. No doubt she was picking some more lavender, for she had already spread a lot of it on a sheet to dry. Wondering whether it were possible to smell both turpentine and lavender at once, I continued my ruminations, sniffing experimentally. How permeated the Studio was with those smells and sounds which gave it special atmosphere and character! Up in my room there was the odour of old leather bindings, wood fires, and floor-polish. Out on the landing at the top of the stairs there was that musty smell which could have come from nowhere but the pigeon-loft, a place frequented by owls also. All the doors shut behind one with a reverberating slam that was essentially their own; the wind had a special way of rattling the windows and booming in the chimney. The red distemper on the staircase walls had become dingily discoloured, but I couldn't imagine it being different. Ever since I could remember, I had been getting that distemper rubbed off on my elbows, and the red paint on the window-seat half-way down was dinted with marks made by my nailed boots in the days when Mr. Moon first began to be our tutor. I had always accepted such familiar phenomena half-consciously, but to-day

296

the place was drawing my attention to its intimate aspects, almost as though I were revisiting it, after an absence of many years, in a mood of mellowed acquaintanceship. The present seemed to have withdrawn for an hour; and there were long silences in which I could almost hear the sound of vanished voices.

My mother's studio had altered very little since the early 'nineties when she put me and my brothers into her serene picture of the Saviour and the little children. The huge plaster figure of the Fighting Gladiator had gone. My mother had decided that he was too much in the way, so he had been broken up and buried in the shrubbery, fig-leaf and all. And the ivy had crept almost half-way across the high, leaded window, without anybody noticing it, apparently. The brown photographs of Italian old masters had faded a little, perhaps, but their backgrounds were as ageless and untroubled as ever; and my mother's paint-brushes were still in the same earthenware pot.

Year after year the sunshine had come and gone, slanting across the floor and along the walls, and taking a little more colour out of the rugs and curtains, while the grandfather clock, with its tuneless strike, ticked slowly on but never kept the right time. There was a patch of sunlight now, exploring the interior of the carved oak cupboard

in which were some old musical instruments tha
had belonged to my father—a viol-de-gamba and
some dim-gilt lutes and guitars. Among them wa
a plaster cast of Grandmama Thornycroft's hand
—that beautifully shaped hand which had done
its Victorian sculpture so well, and now seemed
to symbolize the Thornycroft tradition of fin
craftsmanship. Could I carry on that tradition
with my pen? I wondered, and should I ever write
as good a poem as my mother's picture of *Th*
Hours, where sunset flamed and faded into night
blue sleep that drifted into the flush of daybreak
and the foreground figures swung into the white
radiance of noon? For in that noble design I had
always felt something of the poetry which I could
never put into words; and in it I could recognize
my kinship with the strength and simplicity of m
mother's imaginations.

To be a painter, it seemed to me, was a mor
fortunate occupation than to be a poet. Up in m
book-room there was nothing I could be engrossed
in unless I were mentally excited; and poetr
more often came into my head when I was out o
doors. But down here my mother had alway
created an atmosphere of contentment while sh
was at work, humming half under her breath a
she put in her controlled brush-strokes with a
absorbed and intent forgetfulness of her surround

ngs, or getting down from the painting-steps now and again to have a good look at what she'd been doing. Uncle Hamo was just the same. By a side door, one went quietly in to his immense studio, passing among a crowd of statuary figures, busts and bas-reliefs; and there he was in his white smock chiselling calmly at some marble head, himself the living portrait of a master craftsman. Only a few weeks ago I had been to see him. He had been very kind, and had said nothing about my failure at the University. It had been a memorable visit, for I had found him at work on his first sketch for the seated figure of Tennyson which he was to make for the ante-chapel of Trinity, Cambridge. While I was talking to him, he took Tennyson's old black hat and cloak out of a cupboard and suggested that I should try how they fitted me. The hat, with its enormously wide brim, made me feel rather ridiculous; but I considered it a stroke of luck to have had it on my head.

I could see that Uncle Hamo was amused by the self-conscious solemnity with which I wrapped the cloak, so green with age, around me. 'Let us hope that some day you will have no need to borrow the mantle of greatness, old man,' he remarked. I replied that I feared my head would never be half as large as Tennyson's, as well I might, since the hat came down over my nose like an extinguisher.

Nevertheless I felt secretly elated afterwards as I
walked away along the Melbury Road with my
new straw hat in my hand. For Uncle Hamo had
spoken of my printed poems as though he believed
in me. 'Let your thoughts ring true; and always
keep your eye on the object while you write,' he
had said. Which, although I wasn't altogether
aware of it, was what I hadn't hitherto done.

*   *   *

Into the Sunday morning silence of the studio
buzzed a bumble-bee. After a droning tour of my
mother's canvases it settled to investigate some
marigolds in a jam-jar on the shelf above the fireplace, where there was a photograph of *The Birth
of Eve*, which I had always attributed to Michel-
angelo but was really by Watts. With my cus-
tomary benevolence toward bumble-bees I captured it in my handkerchief and sent it sailing
through the little side-window which looked on
to the lawn. Hearing a sound of conversation from
down by the herbaceous border, I went out to
reconnoitre the identity of my mother's visitors.
From behind a yew hedge I ascertained that it was
only dear old Major Horrocks and his deaf sister
who had walked up the hill for a chat and a toddle
round the garden. They were now primed and

ready to wish me many happy returns of the day, and the Major produced a jocularity about my having attained my majority without having yet become a major. This had to be written on his sister's tablet after my mother had failed to transmit it by finger language.

'Edgeworth's little jokes are almost bad enough to be good ones,' remarked Miss Clara in that queer quavering uncontrolled voice of hers which she hadn't overheard for more than fifty years. In her youth she had been beautiful, and the face which looked out from her black poke-bonnet had beauty still. The decades had made a masterpiece of it, carving lines of character, and refining her features to an essential austerity over which played her expressive liveliness, while her eyes watched our lips with the lonely questioning of deafness. She was now more than ninety; but her hand, grasping a knobbed ebony stick, signified an indomitable alertness of spirit that had carried her well into a new century which she seemed to find quite as interesting as the last one.

The Major, with his trimmed white beard and rubicund complexion, had an inexhaustible supply of good humour. His style of dress comfortably epitomized the oddity and distinction of a well-connected country gentleman who farmed a few hundred acres, was an authority on rock-plants and flowering shrubs, and loved good music and the fine arts in an unaffected way.

Watching him as he praised my mother's tea-roses and condoled with her over the mysterious failure of this year's lilies, I wondered how he would have behaved had his military career obliged him to take part in a battle. I couldn't imagine him meeting the enemy on any except hob-nobbing terms, or bringing down anything more formidable than a pheasant.

Meanwhile the warm air was aromatic with the musky smells of the autumn garden; trails of gossamer wavered silkily across vistas of sunshine, and everything seemed imbued with reluctance to do more than doze on into an idle afternoon. These old friends of ours hadn't changed very much since my childhood, I thought. I had looked up at them for the first time as I played on this sloping path, where I sniffed the scent of June from the tree-peonies which hung large white heads after a shower of rain. Now I was several inches higher than Major Horrocks; and here we all were, pottering loquaciously down toward the alcove by the vinery, where Miss Horrocks would take a few minutes rest before walking home. My mother, with an armful of lavender, was reminding the Major of how I'd once squirted him with the greenhouse syringe; and he, with an appreciative chuckle, had halted to relight his cheroot with a sputtering fusee; and the black Persian cat Ranji, who had sociably accompanied us, was staring up at him with tolerant curiosity. Too young for subtleties of detached perception, I vaguely shared Ranji's feeling that it was all very leisurely and delightful. I could not be conscious of such a moment, as I should be to-day, as a memory already recovered from the dreaming distance of bygone experience; nor could I realize that our transient voices and matter-of-course doings were somehow significant and permanent in that Elysian harmony of mood and weather where nothing seemed to disturb our neighbourly simplicities, and all else was less than a rumour from beyond the blue horizon of the Weald.

But the Major was saying what a gay young spark he'd been when he was young and wore a kilt in his militia regiment. Poking me in the ribs with a gouty finger, he informed me that when he was in his twenties he hadn't allowed the grass to grow under his feet. '*Carpe diem*—or catch your fish while you can see them,' he concluded. And then 'Edgeworth, Edgeworth,' came in bird-like quaverings from Miss Horrocks in the Virginia-creeper-covered alcove: 'We shall be late for luncheon, you bad boy!' And my mother came out of the vinery with an enormous bunch of grapes which she presented to the Major. Leaving me to see them off, she departed to the studio with her cargo of lavender.

As we walked along the kitchen-garden Major Horrocks remarked that it was one of the worst years for wasps he'd ever known. Plucking a golden plum, he dislodged about a dozen of them from its excavated recesses, and then made a feeble but engaging joke about the wasp being father to the thought.

'What thought?' I inquired. 'The thought of getting stung, I suppose,' he replied, chucking the plum into a black-currant bush.

Down in Gedges Wood the pigeons crooned contentment as though they knew that it was Sunday and my birthday, and as though for them all else was oblivion. Past the melon-frames and the cucumber-frames and the miniature forest of the asparagus-bed we went; past the raspberry canes and the rhododendron thicket which had formerly been overlooked by the fort. The Major stopped to inspect a bird-cherry tree which he had planted for my mother in the 'eighties. It was doing nicely, he observed; and the hum of insects from its foliage concurred with his opinion.

When they had gone out by the garden gate, I stood in the shadow of the old leaning may-tree and watched them till they disappeared round the corner of the road by the stables. They were rather like the old century, I thought, going down the hill with so much of it in their heads and so little of the new one left to them. But the future was mine, or as much of it as I could get for myself. Anything might happen in the next fifty years, though I had no idea what sort of things they would be.

Meanwhile this September morning looked as if nothing could change its meridian prosperity. As I turned to go up to the house, I couldn't imagine what it would feel like to be more than twenty-one. Lucky to be in love with life, I did not know how lucky I was.